THE FOUR-ACRE

THE FOUR-ACRE

BY

J. C. BADCOCK

ILLUSTRATED BY THE AUTHOR

PHOENIX HOUSE

LONDON

THE FOUR-ACRE

A RABBIT screamed as my brother took it from the wire snare. It struggled in his hands and lashed out viciously with its long hind legs, tearing a red weal on his arm, and when Brad saw this he swore softly and pressed out the animal's neck.

'An old buck,' he said as I stood watching him. 'Gor! He'll take a devil of a lot of stewing.'

We reset the snare and went over the meadows, our prize hanging unobtrusively down the inside of my trouser leg.

Respectfully we touched our forelocks to the farmer whom we passed as we approached the gateway and wished him 'Good evening', and he grunted an unintelligible reply.

Of course it was out of season work, this rabbit snaring, for it was the month of May; the R's of the months had slipped by in snow and frost and high wind, but Brad held that there was

no close season for conies, and his view was staunchly sup-
ported by my mother who, by force of economic pressure, was
a realist. Food of any kind was very acceptable at our family
table, and much came from the fields.

On this evening it was warm. Many weeks earlier I had
pitched my tent in the four-acre field near to the canal, before
the last drift of snow had gone and whilst yet the wind was
bending the fine tall elms.

But I had been very impatient, and at last my parents had
given way to my pleadings. I had a sound argument too.

'Fresh air,' the doctor had advised some time earlier. 'Fresh
air. That's what he should have,' and I used this to support
my case.

Father had shrugged his shoulders, a little disinterested, and
said that I could do as I pleased.

'If he wants to starve in a field, that's his affair, the young
fool.' But my mother's objections were not so easily overcome.
However, one fine day, a day that carried a promise of spring,
she half-heartedly agreed, although full of apprehension and
good advice.

'Take plenty of clothes,' she said. 'Must you sleep on that
wretched bag of straw? It's horrible!' I could never convince
her that my bag of straw was the warmest bed of all.

'Don't try to "do" for yourself. Come home for your meals.'

I promised, but both of us knew that it was only a formality.

'If your cough gets worse you'll have to come back home,'
she warned. 'Take your foalsfoot syrup!'

I inwardly swore that my pecking cough should not be
heard by a soul and that the sickly syrup should be buried deep
in the latrine trench after I had dug it out; or, better still,
spread upon a wand of hawthorn to entice the night-flying
moths, those soft bat-chased things of the dark. I certainly
would not touch it.

On the first night of my camping there was a frost which solidified the dew on the cocksfoot and made the puddles in the hoof-holes crackle as the freezing water became firm, and I—too used to the stuffiness of an airless bedroom during the past several months—shivered under the canvas and snuggled deeper into the comfort of the straw bag, sleeping fitfully through the long night.

The next day a sudden change in temperature took away the ice from the cow-puddles and the ditch-drinks, and brought a slanting rain and wind, wind that tore at the tent lanyards and threatened to pull the pegs from the ground, and this despite the fact that I was sheltered in the lee of a scrawny elm hedge.

It is strange that the prophecy of March is so often incorrect. Many times the lion and lamb fable is reversed, and then it is a devil of a lamb that chases March into the tears of April.

But now the winds and bluster and peevishness had gone and it was May and summer to come again, and a lifetime to live and more; for a summer is a lifetime to the young. The ageing live meanly through all seasons; they live not a day but regret that it has gone; and a summer month—a June hour—is quickly spent when it would be niggardly hoarded.

But for Brad and me the May days were golden and spent lavishly, as though the full purse were bottomless.

The body of the rabbit pressed warmly against my leg as we walked over the fields to my tent, and yet it did not interfere with my gait, for I had become accustomed to carrying game in this manner. Many a time both of us had passed under the scrutinizing eyes of Peabody, the policeman, with a rabbit concealed within each leg of our trousers, but our upright walk had created no suspicion in his mind; the fact that we were who we were always caused him to doubt.

We mashed tea and ate at the side of the stick fire until the light faded, until young couples began to wander slowly down the Cowclose path, not as lovers, but carelessly, stooping now and then to pluck daisy heads to throw at each other, and to chase and be chased; to be caught and held, a little breathlessly, embarrassed by May thoughts.

After the capture they would walk more sedately over the close to the bridge and lean on the waist-high parapet, drawing nearer to each other as the mist rose on the water and dimitty light fell.

It was strange how sweethearts chose the bridge by the canal for their love-making, for there were many ghosts there; many phantoms mixed with the mists in that quiet restful spot. Harassed to death people sometimes came from the village to bring their troubles to the silent water below the bow bridge, and there they found peace for themselves, but left phantoms which made the lovers shudder a little when they looked over the parapet into the dark pool under the bridgeside hawthorn.

Often life had its beginning on the bridge, and its end below.

We sat until the first star appeared, speaking little, but listening to the soft night noises; and when the owls became noisy Brad rose to go, and in a while I was alone in the quiet of the night.

From the bridge there came a slight scuffle on the gravelled walk, a boy and girl laughed breathessly and were silent again; and soon I heard the squeak of the bridle-gate as Brad passed through to the village, for the hinges were rusty and talkative, tell-tale to all who went that way. Until the moon had hung over the elms of Amberdale, the gate creaked out over the fields, intermittently, as the lovers went home, and at last the night was left to me and the owls; for them to hunt, for me to sleep.

The voles came to search for food-bits, pressing under the tent walls and foraging in among the odds and ends at the side of my straw mattress, but they did not disturb me, for they are

the night companions of all meadow sleepers; and, in listening
to their excited whispers and the higher quarrelsome squeals of
the shrews, I fell asleep.

The moon had passed its zenith when I awoke with a start,
and the light was low on the meadows, coming to the hedge-
trees at an angle so that there were many moon-shadows, and
low-flying barn owls were black and white in the moonlight
where earlier they had been soft buff.

I lay awake for a moment listening and wondering what had
caused me to wake so abruptly; but I could hear nothing
except the little ones of the night searching for food.

A droning beetle sang from the distance, crashed into the
tent panels with a thump and slid down the canvas to the grass,
but in a little while he rose again and went noisily on his way.

A sheep coughed in the dark, an almost human sound,
frightening to those unused to it, but there was nothing to fear.
I had coughed with them at times when there was a dampness
in the meadows. Theirs was nothing to fear.

I could not sleep again and tried to think of the reason. The
night was normal, or so it seemed; and yet there was something
indefinably queer about it, an unsettledness that I rarely
experienced when alone, for I preferred life that way.

I sat up on my mattress and listened intently, not satisfied
that all was well, vaguely suspicious; and suddenly I realized
that I was not alone in the four-acre on that May night.

A cow belched noisily and grunted, and I knew that it had
been disturbed. I knew too that the sheep had risen from the
grass, for I heard the thud of the lead-ewe as it stamped its foot
on the ground in warning, and soon the small flock scampered
a few paces to a mound in a corner of the field, their uncut
tags echoing like castanets.

I peered beneath the wall of the tent but could see no one;
and yet there appeared to be a shadow by the distant haw

hedge, a dull shape in the dim moonlight near to where the sheep were gathered.

'It's nonsense!' I tried to reassure myself. 'Moon madness,' but only mouthed the words; no sound came from my lips.

From the village a dog howled mournfully, the dreadful noise ending in a whimpering wail, and after that there was no noise in the meadows.

The voices and the shrews had left the food papers on the floor and vanished like night fairies at dawn; and I felt afraid, not of the darkness or the loneliness, but of something much less tangible; some vague apprehension had invaded my heart and, try as I might, I could not shake it off.

I lay back on my bed and waited. There was a faint tease of wayside weeds as though someone was walking stealthily over the longer bents by the hedgerow.

I had erected a barbed-wire fence around my camp site in order to keep the inquisitive cattle away, and now, as I lay with prickly skin, I heard the grate of the wire as it was pressed down in its staples, and realized that someone was climbing through the fence.

Instantly my hand went out towards my snake-stick which lay on the floor of the tent, and I felt a little calmer when my fingers came into contact with it.

'Now', I thought, 'I can put up a fight if necessary.'

Still I could not conceive why anyone should want to interfere with me, and yet, I reasoned, it must be someone up to no good or there would be no need for such stealth.

The hair began to rise in the nape of my neck as I heard the intruder's fingers feeling for the tent opening, a scratching noise on the taut canvas, like a mouse under a skirting board.

Silently I rose from my bed—an incongruous figure in a short-tailed shirt and with skinny bare legs—and prepared to give battle.

Slowly the aperture parted and let in the blue light of the
moon, and in the tent gap appeared the head of a man. I could
not discern his features, for he was in silhouette, but gently I
raised my snake-stick as one would a javelin, and at last found
my voice.

'Who are you?' I asked. 'I'll stick you if you come a step
nearer.'

The figure gasped, then let out a surprised laugh.

'Boyo!' it said. 'Boyo! You! Well I'm damned!' And in
that moment all the fear went from my heart, and I murmured
weakly and a little tearfully, 'Bronco! Oh, Bronco!'

Soon I had undone the lacing of the tent, and my visitor
sat with me on the bed; and we laughed uproariously in the
shaft of moonlight which the open flap admitted.

Bronco was a tramp, a roving vagabond who frequently
came to the village for a few days and passed on again. He
explained how he came to be in the four-acre.

'On'y come hereabouts this afternoon, boyo. Wandered
around a bit, then took to the fields for a night's doss. Wuz on
mi' way to the tunnel barn when I saw this tent. Thought it wor
left by some boys or somebody. I reckoned it'd be empty and
I'd sleep in it for the night. I came steady-like in case there was
somebody about. Then I found you. Oh, boyo!' and we both
collapsed again in laughter, for he was easy to laugh with.

He made his bed in the tent. From a sacking bag he produced
a sheet of tattered waterproof which he carelessly wrapped
around his lean body and, with the bag for pillow, lay on the
padded grass of the tent floor.

'Why don't you undress?' I asked. 'You must be mighty
uncomfortable,' but he only grinned and looked at my skinny
bare legs.

In a short time he was asleep, breathing softly as a child,
and I too settled down in comfort, all strange fears gone now;

and when I awoke again it was birdsong and dawn and my companion was already at the pyramid of blazing sticks, boiling the water for breakfast tea.

Bronco was a strange man; a natural outcast. As regularly as the cuckoo he came to the village. In the early spring, 'on my way through' as he put it, and again at the time when the thistles were getting a little out of hand in the grazing pastures, he would turn up in his old haunts; the tumbledown, roofless remains of a brick field-barn where he slept when the nights were windy; or the tunnel formed by the overgrowing bushes in the blackthorn spinney where he could lie safe from the rain.

I was very attached to the old man, for he was a likeable character, a wizened puck of a man who laughed and lied so easily.

He told the most wonderful tales, thrilling adventure stories which held me spellbound, but which I heartily disbelieved; and when I called him a liar he would chide me for my incredulity and laugh, louder and louder, until his voice sailed noisily over the meadows.

The grown-ups tolerated him when he came to the village cadging, for he had a certain charm.

'Can I use your pump, ma'am? I'm that thusty!' and, having received permission, he would fumble with the handle but make no attempt to draw the water.

'Rare good stuff this, ma'am . . . when you've nowt better.' Impressed by Bronco's pathetic appearance many a housewife found enough half-cold tea left over from a previous meal to fill the old man's dingy can.

Bronco was no ordinary tramp; he was not afraid of work. Each year he came to seek for a job for a few weeks on the large farm which stood to the south of the village, and always he was engaged, given a long scythe and told to clear the thistles from this field and that, for which the farmer paid him a small weekly wage, quite inadequate for the amount of work done, but Bronco did not complain.

'You departed last year without receiving your just dues,' the farmer would say importantly—he was a very formal, straight-laced man, a deacon, or a warden, or something, I forget which—and Bronco would spit on the few shillings and thrust them into a pocket hidden in the depths of an alarming thickness of clothes.

'I got restless last year, mister, and went wi' out my ha'pence,' he would say apologetically. 'I left the knife'—indicating the scythe—'under the big elum in the twelve-acre. Did you find it?'

When one day the farmer reproved him again, and spoke grandly to him, Bronco shook his head and said sorrowfully: 'I ain't a plant, mister! I can't stick to one place! I get fidgety! But I'm all right now. I'm going to settle here. People is nice hereabouts.'

When I heard of his intention I rejoiced; but within a week or two Bronco had gone, leaving nothing but the ashes of his fire, cold and scattered by the blackthorn bushes, and his unclaimed wages.

The farmer's face became sterner than ever when he heard the news, for he was angry at the loss of such cheap labour.

'A wretched man,' he said grandly. 'Doomed, I'm afraid, to hell,' and as he raised his face piously to the sky I wondered, and inwardly disagreed.

Brad and I were lacking in that theological erudition which children are so often expected to share with the saints, and our picture of the hereafter was not, perhaps, as clear as our teachers would have wished it to be, standing as it did somewhere between the problematically better and an attractively worse world than the one in which we lived.

When we thought of it at all, we imagined heaven as a place

where the great folk went when they died, the grand austere
people who cleared their throats noisily and never smiled; or
the pale invalids, the sad ones who wore greatcoats perpetually.
We thought of hell as a kind of corner in which we would be
put, face to the wall, if we swore. Our teachers told us there
was nothing more, that was all; but in our hearts we knew that
there was an in-between place reserved for the folk who
laughed and lied—the charming people; folk like old Bronco
with whom we found no fault.

Like most wanderers he did not know his age.

'Getting on, boyo! Getting on!' he used to say when I
questioned him.

As time went by I noticed a change in the old fellow. He still
laughed uproariously at nothing, bursting out into a wild peal
of mirth after we had sat silent for some while, and his joy was
as that of the larks in the meadow grass, for they also sing for
no reason.

But there appeared a little sadness in his eyes at times and,
oblivious to the rest of the world, he would stare out into the
distance where the bright evening light was on the horizon,
and at such times I would quietly leave him and go to my tent,
closing the field gate softly behind me, careful not to disturb
him.

One year he failed to appear, and the villagers shook their
heads. The thistles were cut down by the mowing-machine,
and Bronco's scythe was hung in a corner of the barn.

Another year went by and still no Bronco, and I gave him
up for lost, thinking that he had perhaps died in some turnpike
poorhouse. But I was wrong.

A bronze-faced Romany gave me glad news of him as she
leaned from the half-door of her painted wagon.

'A little fellow?' She repeated my inquiry. 'What's he
done?'

I assured her that I sought the old man as a friend, and she told me of his whereabouts.

'Saw him in the Loddington Gap, in the old mere road. My people kicked him out of the lane and he went up'ards to the goss common. Reckon he'll still be there.'

I thanked her and wished her *Kusko bok*.

I found him as she had said, sitting in the lee of a gravel pit. By his side was a mongrel dog which growled as I approached, but a word from the old man soothed the animal.

It seemed that Bronco now possessed his own transport, a derelict old perambulator which he had obviously picked off some rubbish tip and which now stood packed with all the old man's worldly possessions.

'Bronco!' I yelled, so glad to see him again.

He rose a little unsteadily and came towards me. I held out my hand.

'Bronco! How are you?'

'Boyo!' he cried. 'Why, it's boyo!' And he laughed long and loudly as of old.

'I'm retired now, y' know,' he informed me after we had settled by his fire.

I indicated the dog.

'Ah!' said Bronco. 'I've got a lurcher too. Good dog that. He gets harnessed to my pram and helps to pull it. I'm getting a bit old now, boyo! I am, you know!'

We sat and talked and laughed and lied; yes, he hadn't forgotten how to tell the tale.

I remarked upon the dog's limp, a slight dropping of one of its legs.

'Ah! he did it last summer. Bad business that wor! It wor this way,' and he went on to explain the misadventure.

'It was atop o' Fawley Hill where it happened. Leastways that's where it began. It finished a sight lower down.'

B

He paused to pull at his pipe, too tightly filled with tobacco.

'Ah, yes! The dog! Well, we'd pulled up to the top of the hill—and it wor hard work too, boyo, I'm telling you—and we were having a bit of a rest, like. I had just nipped over the hedge to . . .' he hesitated. 'Well, you know how things are.' I nodded understandingly.

'I reckon a rabbit must ha' stirred or summat. I got to the gate to see my dog tearing down the hill, the pram after him, and it worn't long before it caught up wi' him neither; and soon, right from where we had only just pulled our load, the whole lot lay all over the place; pram, dog, togs, tins—everything. Boyo! I could ha' cried. And mi' dog had a brukken leg and I had to load him on to the pram wi' the rest of the stuff and pull the whole damn lot back again up Fawley by meself. Gor! Boyo! I never leave mi' pram now wi'out tying up my dog first. Taught me a lesson, that did.'

Long into the evening we talked, and when I rose to go old Bronco held out a gnarled hand and said goodbye in a low voice, and much of the mirth had gone from his eyes. Our parting made a deep impression on me, leaving me sad and depressed.

That was the last time that I saw Bronco.

He died in a ditch and his dog howled over him. When they took the body away to the village to await the coroner's verdict, the dog still howled to the moon from the spot where its master had lain for so long in the ditch.

An irate farmer—work-tired and half mad with the disturbance—blew out the animal's brains, and then there was peace in the night.

I was very shocked when I heard of the passing of Bronco, for he had shared my tent on a night when I had been afraid a year or so before. He took much laughter away with him.

BRAD and I spent almost all our time in the fields. Our home at the old Manor House was only a kind of retreat to which we could go when we wished. Brad actually slept there throughout the whole of the year, and was apt to deride my desire to get away from bricks and mortar to my tent in the meadow corner.

'I believe you'd sleep there through the blooming winter if they'd let you,' he often said—the 'they' being my parents—but I could not agree, for winter in the country's heart is a

13

hard thing. I was glad enough of the comfort of my mother's home in the dragging days when the sun was so thrifty and light lasted but an hour or so.

But in the spring, when the first kingcups appeared, then I grew restless for the four-acre.

We spent a grudging time at school, an unnecessary time so we thought, for, as Brad said, we learned nothing there but sums and essays and suchlike things, and so we often stayed away, only to be punished for our truancy by the master on the following morning. But neither the crime nor the punishment was very great in those easy days.

We took many things from the woods and meadows, for we had grown up with the fixed idea that all wild creatures were fair game and belonged to no man but the one who could catch them.

Whatever skill we had acquired in the art of snaring and trapping—and Brad's ability in this direction was considerable —was due in no small measure to our long experience in the art of escape.

Both old Peabody, the policeman, and the stern-faced keeper had a quite different interpretation of *meum and teum* to ours. We rarely trespassed on the large estate over which the latter had prowling rights, for we had a mighty respect for the gun which he always carried slung in the crook of his arm, and in consequence we kept well out of his way. Instead we glared at one another from a distance, he from the Nether Wood beside the hedge which divided the estate from old Smithers' top field, and we in comparative safety on the far side of the same hedge, but not near enough to be within range of shot.

Brad detested the keeper, and not without reason, for he had once deprived him of his best snare wires. Brad had set the long hedge for rabbits.

'Look at these blooming runs!' he said one afternoon.

'Must be scores of conies there. Pity to let them all go to the Hall. They'll never 'preciate them. Come on! We'll set for 'em,' and cautiously we had crept along the hedgerow, pegging down the wire loops firmly in the yellow clay of the stoles, careful not to disturb the rabbits grazing in the adjoining field, for they were our intended victims.

The work completed, we backed slowly, silently, through the cover-shrubs until we came to the cart-rut road. There we climbed the rickety fence and sprinted away from the wood to the safety of the meadow which lay outside the confines of the estate, and from there we looked over to the hedge in which the snares were set.

Suddenly Brad swore softly and muttered under his breath.

'What's the matter?' I asked.

He put a hand on my shoulder, forcing me lower in the nettle clump in which we lay hidden.

'Look at that!' he whispered. 'Just our luck!'

The grazing rabbits had scuttled hastily from their feeding, but, instead of making for the runs in which the snares had been so expertly laid, they divided, one group passing to the right, the other to the left; and following Brad's gaze I saw the reason.

Beyond the hedge, in the half-light of the cover-shrubs, stood the bulky keeper, his gun in its usual position on the crook of his arm.

I tried to get even lower on to the ground, dropping my head on to the damp turf, hoping that not seeing I would be unseen.

The nettles stung my face into a burning heat, but I did not notice the pain in my anxiety to be hidden from the man with the gun. Those things terrified me, not, I think, from the hurt that they might have done me—although I was very conscious of this—but because of the appalling noise they made. There is not one noise in the country like the shot of a gun, not even the first crack of a waist-wide elm branch, snapped off on a still winter night under its burden of snow.

Brad hissed through his teeth.

'Look at him! Just look at him!' and the venom in his voice made me raise my head a little, and there through the nettle-stems I saw the keeper bend down and methodically pull the snares from the ground, carefully wrap the wire around the holding stakes, and put the lot in the capacious bag which was slung at his side.

Brad was almost in tears with rage.

'My snares!' he cried. 'He's got my snares. They were my best too. The thief! Oh, the blooming thief!'

I laid a restraining hand on him, for, truth to tell, I thought that he might give away our hide so great was his temper, but in a moment he quietened down.

The keeper came to the lichen-clad fence, away from the gloom of the wood, and we watched him as he looked search-ingly over the field, shading his eyes from the lowering sun. For a long time his gaze rested on the nettle clump in which we lay, and I thought that he had detected our hide.

'Still!' warned Brad. 'Don't move! Keep still!' I squinted through the nettles at the figure by the stile and my heart gave a lurch, for slowly the keeper raised the gun to his shoulder and suddenly the world was filled with a dreadful, baleful noise, a coarse belch of sound that re-echoed through the thickness of the woodland, and from somewhere in the sky a black rag of feathers dropped awkwardly on to the grass hummocks of the meadow.

I would have yelled at the awful racket, but it had com-pletely petrified me, which was perhaps a blessing for both of us.

The carrion crow lay where it had fallen, and the keeper,

satisfied, went back through the thick undergrowth to become lost to our view.

When I had recovered a little I turned to Brad and said, 'Gosh! I thought he was shooting at us. And it was only an old crow,' and we laughed silently in the nettles, laughed quietly until the tears ran down our cheeks, but more in relief than mirth.

Then Brad remembered his snares and his temper returned.

'The rotter!' he fumed. 'The thief! To pinch my snares! The rogue!'

'It's all right,' I soothed. 'We'll make some more. Let's go now!' I was anxious to be away from the vicinity of the dreadful gun, and after a cautious look over the fieldways and the hedgerows Brad rose gently and beckoned to me, and we went to our home.

But he never forgave the theft of his snares.

Both Brad and I were, however, too well aware of the danger to attempt any sort of revenge on the keeper. We knew that the farther away from the estate we kept, the better it would be, and in consequence we became more discreet than valorous.

In any case we were in no way dependent upon the game of those particular few acres for our pickings. There were many fields in which we could roam in comparative safety, for most of the smaller farmers looked upon us with a fairly tolerant eye if, at times, a little suspiciously. They had no fancy game to nurture; no pheasants to pet and fuss over; only the common ground-game, the rabbit—that vermin of the countryside— and a few escapee partridges; and we were as much in the fields as were they. As the kestrel took the bank-vole, so we took the rabbit and an occasional bird, all for the same purpose—food.

True, we caught the bullfinch on our limed twigs in the winter time when the sale of the captives was often our only source of pocket-money, as was sometimes the case when other predators—more adept than we—had depleted the ranks of the conies and made the capture of the few that were left a chancy business for us.

We were always sure of the bullfinches. They were such stupid birds.

I had only to sit in the leaf mould of the hedge bottom and squeak a mild little call 'Pee-u . . . Pee-u', and a red-breasted male would come seeking a rival, only to founder on the sticky twigs, after which Brad would come along with a drop or two of paraffin, clean the lime from the wings of the birds and put them into the security of his pocket, there to be carried home, wonted, and sold to the local dealer.

Peabody took little exception to this, neither did the other, grander people of the village, for it was one of those many practices which were often accepted without question in the country and not thought too much about.

But bird-catching had to cease at Valentine's Day. Then the birds had chosen their mates and were free to their love until the November fogs as far as we were concerned.

And I was glad. I was never very fond of my part in the snaring of them, for they so often died from the shock of such rough treatment; and then as their frail bodies quivered and the film fell over their bright eyes I felt afraid, as though I had been careless with something precious.

Sometimes I would take a little spittle on the end of my finger and try to force it down the bill of the dying bird in an effort to restore it to life, but, irrevocably, the grey film would obliterate the bright spot in the eye, and the head fall awkwardly over the edge of my palm.

At such a time Brad would look at me in a curious way and say rather gruffly:

'It's no good, it's dead! Can't be helped!'

I was always glad when Valentine's Day came and we should no longer take the birds on the lime.

But now there were other things to interest us. The peewits were nesting in the fallow fields and on the grazing land, and there was always a ready market for their eggs among the gourmets of the village—the doctor, the retired school officer, the pensioned shepherd crippled with rheumatism. There were plenty of these delicacies to be gathered for the finding.

My brother and I crossed the plank bridge over the stream, crouched by the side of the hawthorn bush on the opposite bank and peered over the untidy stretch of fallow land.

'See if you can see their heads!' said Brad, but in the maze of hummocks and covered moleheaps it was almost impossible to detect the sitting peewits.

I could see nothing of the birds at all and told him so.

'Can you?' I asked, and he had to admit that the birds were too well hidden by their natural camouflage for him to see.

He urged his body forward round the bush and shaded his eyes, but still there was no sign of the birds until, from the sky above, came a shrill call.

'Pee-u-wit wit. Pee-u-wit,' and, as we turned our heads instinctively to look in the direction of the sound, the air rang with more cries as the nesting birds rose from the secret places in the field and joined the alarm bird.

Brad cursed roundly.

'Did you see where they came from?' he demanded, and I had to admit that I had not. But then neither had he.

'We'll never find the nests now,' he said glumly, and I knew he was right, for so closely do the eggs of the lapwing merge with the earth upon which they are laid that it is almost impossible to find them except by pure accident.

Our usual way of detection was to try to observe the sitting birds at nest, and, if that failed, to watch from which particular spot they arose when disturbed. In this we were not always successful, for quite often the peewit would quietly leave her eggs and run a dozen or so yards away before rising from the ground. Because of this we were frequently deceived.

We searched carefully each ridge of weathered earth, and the peewits dived frantically at us, calling broken-heartedly above our heads, but we took little notice of them, for this was their habit and meant very little but that they were annoyed at the disturbance.

A lark sang overhead, and its voice threaded through the pathetic calls of the peewits like a strand of silk through coarser stuff, and, when my foot would have trodden on a tiny heap of pebbles, I saw that they were a clutch of earth-brown eggs, and because of this I stumbled in avoiding them and fell to my knees. Suddenly the lark's song ceased and the bird circled high in the sky, higher almost than sight, and silently wheeling and watching.

Kneeling there on the bare earth I waited for the music to begin again, but there was nothing in the sky but harassed peewit calls.

I have never forgotten that moment when the soaring sky-lark ceased his song as I sprawled over the scrap of a nest.

'What's up?' inquired Brad. 'What have you done?'

I rose from my knees and pointed to the eggs. 'Look at them! Larks'!' I answered. 'Gosh! Ain't they cunning?'

But Brad shrugged his shoulders impatiently. 'What good are they? Come on! Find the peewits'. We'll get something for the plovers', nothing for the larks'.'

In country nomenclature they were peewits' eggs until gathered, but became plovers' eggs when they were to be sold. It somehow sounded better that way.

We left the lark's nest untouched, and when we were a few feet away the wheeling bird sang again above the calls and alarms of the peewits and things were normal once more, no dumb witness accusingly silent from the blue sky.

We walked the whole length of the field, then back again, and again, and again, until I think there was not a yard we had not examined, and yet we found no peewit's nest.

'I'm tired of this,' I complained. 'There's no nests!'

Brad pointed to the fidgeting peewits. 'What are they doing, then?' he demanded. 'Think they're up there for fun? There's nests about, I tell you!' He dropped his voice. 'They only want finding.'

We made our way towards the rising ground to the pair of lock gates which spanned the weedy canal, and on the broad arm of one of these we sat, a little disgruntled.

'Nothing! The whole of the afternoon,' muttered Brad. 'Nothing for all our work,' ignoring the song of the willow-wren and the warm sun, the music of the insects.

As we sat there, prodding the screw-moss in the joints of the brickwork with the toes of our boots, the peewits settled again, first at the bottom end of the field, farthest away from us, then —as though forgiving us our sins and no longer afraid of us— those nearer dropped on to the coarse ground and disappeared among the clods of earth, and their petulant calls were no longer heard in the sky, only the lark song was left up there, and the willow-warbler in the canal thicket, and the red-backed bees in the keck heads.

My brother stirred slightly and breathed a quiet 'Ah!' and I would have spoken, but he raised his finger in warning and pointed to the mound of soil a few yards away; and there, low to the ground, squatted a brooding peewit.

I burst into a roar of laughter, and the bird ran away for a distance before rising with a loud cry.

'At our feet!' I cried in delight. 'Oh, lor'! At our feet,' and we walked quickly over to the nest.

There were four eggs lying on a few rough bits of dried grass, quite open to the sky yet so coloured as to be almost indistinguishable from the scattered plough pebbles.

In a moment Brad was on his knees by the nest, his handkerchief unfolded on the ground beside him, but as he picked up the first egg he grimaced and weighed it carefully in his hand and frowned.

'No good!' he said at last.

'Why?' I asked. 'Have they been sat on?'

He nodded. 'Yes! There's young 'uns inside, almost ready for hatching. Can tell by the weight of 'em. Heavy as lead!'

Suddenly he turned to me and a broad grin creased his face and, for so little reason, we laughed again, loudly over the fieldways.

'All afternoon!' Brad slapped his thigh. 'All afternoon and nothing to show for it. What a frazzle!'

Our voices joined in the mirth of the larks and the rest of the birds as we walked unsteadily over the lock gates to the towpath, and soon we forgot our small disappointment and our laughter as we went by the canal side towards my tent.

Brad usually came along to the tent in the evenings. For hours we would sit in the summer, quietly there with little talk, content to listen to the rest of that small world, and to watch the comings and goings of the meadow ways.

We had seen the chaffinch bringing nesting material to the haw hedge in the earlier days of the summer; the grass-bits and the mosses and the coloured lichens, all the decorations of nature with which to ornament her nest; and now, the eggs laid and hatched, we had watched her, evening after evening, take food to her family, and we knew that soon her work would be ended and her young would stand unsteadily on the wire of the hedge-fence looking out into their strange world.

We had witnessed the same thing with the dunnock a few

days earlier, but neither of us had commented on it beyond a delighted indrawing of breath when the fluff-feathered nestlings had first appeared with their fussing parents.

Our way along the canal side was unhurried; there was no reason for haste; the evening and the night were yet to come.

Brad rarely travelled fast in the open—unless of course he was being chased—for he required time to take in all that the country could tell him. He never missed a rabbit run in the hedgerow, or a hare's form in the meadow grass, and often I have seen him stop dead before a clump of fog-grass, gently press aside the blades to reveal a nest of the field-mouse, a rough structure full of tiny blind pink babies, pathetically helpless, anxious for the comfort of their mother, the gentle little creature that Brad held in the cup of his hand, petting with his finger-tip for a moment or two before placing it back again on the young. When the poor-sighted parent would have timidly ran away from the pothering of the day, her babies clutched at her with their gaping mouths, fastening on to her teats, to any part of her fur, in their need. Then Brad would carefully replace the grass-bents over the little frightened family and move away; and I often thought that I had witnessed a near miracle.

The water-voles played noisily in the secretive sedges by the waterside as evening came and we neared the four-acre.

On the facing bricks of one of the low bridges Brad pointed out to me a few wooden pegs that had been driven into the mortar-work, bits of hedge sticks that formed a rough arc over the bow of the bridge.

'See that?' he said. 'That's a bad business!'

I agreed. These were the pegs upon which the people of the narrow-boats hung a long net that entirely covered the bridge span; and in these nets the gaudy kingfisher was entrapped.

We well knew the procedure. As the narrow-boats drew into

the locks one of the younger members of the crew would hurry forward to the chosen bridge—taking a wide detour through the fields so as not to prematurely put up the birds—and there fix his net.

As the boats came from the locks, so the birds would leave their sighting twigs which overhung the water, and fly in easy stages so far ahead of the craft.

The kingfisher, like the midge-hunting swallow, rarely flies over the bridge, but takes the obviously shorter route through the arch, and because of this he is caught in the fine meshes of the snare.

Often the birds fell stunned into the water, but the young bargee, close at hand, would fish them out with his long briar wand and quickly snuff out any lingering life.

I never found out what they did with the lovely birds, whether they were used as ornaments for ladies' hats, or whether the collectors bought them; but they were much sought after by the people of the narrow-boats, and in consequence became very scarce in the district.

After the capture the nets were collected by the oncoming boats and the whole process of part extermination carried on farther up the canal reach.

'It's a bad business!' stormed Brad. 'To take birds like that! They're no good! They can't sing nor nothing!'

I almost reminded him of the bullfinches that we took in the winter, but refrained.

AS WE passed the stile-gap into Four-acre my brother stopped short and looked keenly towards the white tent. Someone was moving among the odds and ends between tent and hedge, and, when the figure came into the open, Brad clicked his tongue in annoyance and pointed.

'Look at that!' he said. 'There's a rare thing!' and he turned away from me and went towards the village.

My heart stood still for a while and a tiredness came to my feet so that they became leaden and cumbersome.

I leaned on a fencing post and a bit of a mist was before my eyes. Foolishly, clumsily, I went forward to meet Mary.

She lowered her head as I approached, and for a while neither of us spoke.

'Hallo, boyo!' she said at last. 'I'm back.'

All I could do was to gape like an idiot. So long ago she had left me in that same meadow, so long ago—and yet not a twelvemonth—that it seemed a lifetime, when she had gone in the evening over into the path of the sun, beyond Ramshorn gate where I had stayed long after she had disappeared.

'We leave tomorrow,' she had said, and my heart dulled at the news. 'We're going away to live, away from the village.'

That was in the autumn, after the swallows had gone, when there were no more flowers to bloom. A few days later I had struck my camp and moved with such reluctance to home.

And now she stood before me again, her velvet eyes looking up shyly from half-lowered lids.

I led her away from the untidiness of the camp site to a wood log near a large elm, nearer to the bushes by the tunnel where she could hear the evensong of the willow-wrens and the excited chatter of the sedge chats; and there we sat, awkwardly, with scarcely anything to say.

She had come on a quite unexpected visit to a remote relative in the village.

'Only for a day or so,' she told me. 'Only till Saturday. I return then.'

It was now mid week.

'I came today,' she replied, in answer to my question. 'I came straight to you.' Her face flushed at the indiscretion.

Sitting there I looked at my worn shoes and my soiled clothes and compared them with the neat trimness of her attire, and she read my thoughts.

'It's all the same,' she said softly. 'I've not changed, boyo! We dress a little different in town, that's all.'

'Tell me of the town!' I asked without eagerness, and she said:

'No! You wouldn't like that!' and I knew that she was

c

right. I had seen but little of it, but what I had seen of the loneliness there had frightened me.

Brad and I had been to the near town only a few months before.

'There's a famous man talking about birds and such things,' said Brad. 'We can find our way to the place. It's free!'

And so we went to the large hall with the big white pillars. Reluctantly the uniformed man at the door had let us in and warned us, 'Just you behave, or else . . .' and he jerked his thumb significantly.

We sat at the back of a large crowd of people and listened whilst a tall gaunt man spoke of birds, many of which I had never heard. But he also talked of the sparrow-hawk and the kestrel, and such an excellent talker was he that I lost much of the point of his lecture in the detailed picture which he painted. His eloquence was such that it conveyed my thoughts away from the stuffed object on the table before him, with which he was illustrating the lecture, to the fields in which it had once lived, and I dreamed a little under the drone of the lecturer's voice.

But the illusion was difficult to maintain for long in the fug and tobacco smoke of that town hall. Amid such a wealth of knowledge I found that I was an exile, far away from the hovering falcon that the rooks chivvied high over the ridge and furrow of the Wranglands pasture.

I had not been to the town again to listen to the bird man and, because of that, lost much that teaching had to offer.

But I had found it hard to give my head to those things; with the heart it was easier for me. And those large bare rooms were so frightening, so vast, that I always felt naked in them. They had not the snugness of the meadows.

The glare-white ceiling seemed to be a bar to the stars, a pale bowl in which was collected the winding tobacco smoke; a fantastically stark sky, full of plaster angels, so far away.

In the fields the night was overhead, almost touchable, near as a friend; and there was nothing between my heart and heaven—except perhaps my head.

I looked again at Mary and pictured her in the town in all her neatness. She was right, I did not want to hear of the town, it was not for me. Yet I felt a little jealous that it should have taken her away from me, and would do so again in a day or two.

We sat on the wood log until the light had almost gone, then walked slowly over the fields to the gateway. There we stayed for a few moments before parting, and, as we stood side by side looking out into the light-line left by the sun, we leaned near to each other until our shoulders lightly touched. With a startled 'Oh!' we drew away again as if stung, and laughed a little awkwardly.

On the morrow, in the afternoon, she came to me again, and I showed her some of the wonders that I had seen.

In the thick hawthorn bush was the cup-nest of the dunnock which held five blue eggs, lovely to look at. I could just see them over the thorns, but Mary, a few inches shorter in height than I, could not glimpse them above the edge of the nest.

'Where?' she inquired. 'I can't see them! Oh!' She over-balanced slightly in attempting to do so and I laughed at her, at which she pouted playfully.

'Hold me then!' she demanded. 'So that I don't fall,' and I placed my hands gingerly at her waist and steadied her, whilst she stood a-tiptoe and peered into the nest.

I felt her slim body move beneath my hands and flushed, and she, turning suddenly and seeing this, gently lowered her heels and faced me.

I did not release my grip at once, and we stood close and still for a moment or two looking at each other, pink of face, two wondering children.

As we wandered towards the tunnel bushes she stooped to pick a clover head, and I picked a few too, to give to her. In the exchange our hands met as we both laughingly tried to bunch the posy, and when we continued our gentle stroll she did not attempt to withdraw her small hand from mine.

So many things we saw that afternoon in the warm sun. We lay and listened to the grasshoppers crinking in the grass and to the droning bees in the honeysuckle tubes; and we had no use for words.

When at last we rose to go from the bushes, we did so reluctantly, and as I gave Mary my hand to assist her to her feet she took it shyly and averted her head, a trifle uncomposed.

In the quiet night I escorted her to the gate across the field where the pathway wound into the village, and we stood again saying our good nights, nearer than last evening and a little more at ease now that the prying day had gone.

'Tomorrow?' I asked.

'Oh yes!' she whispered.

But it was so late when she came to the tent on the morrow that the warmth of day was past and a mist had already formed over the low canal.

I had watched the meadow pathway all through the day, waiting with sinking heart as afternoon faded into quiet evening, not believing the mocking woodpecker. When at last she came from the corner of Ramshorn I ran eagerly to meet her, crying her name, all reserve gone. But as she drew near I could see that something was amiss. Her smile had gone and there was pain in her soft eyes as they looked tragically up at me.

'Mary!' I exploded. 'What is it, Mary? Oh, why are you so late? So little time and the whole afternoon lost!' I said without reproach.

'I have come to say goodbye,' she whispered tearfully. She

put her hand in mine and led me back to the tent, and whereas
yesterday we had found so little to say, now we talked well
into the time of darkness, planning, promising, vowing.

We parted at that same gate. Other couples—older than us
—were strolling towards the small bridge; I could hear the
ashes of the black path crunching beneath their feet and their
subdued laughter which only made me so aware of my own
impending loss.

Mary cried unrestrainedly, and I could not comfort her.
Neither could I frame the word 'Goodbye', and we parted in
silence.

In the morning it was Sunday, and the single bell of the church
tolled monotonously, calling the well-dressed folk to early
service. At mid morning the bell rang again and children walked
sedately up the hill to give thanks in the house of God, but they
had no sun to walk with, for, after a watery burst at dawn, it
had hidden behind a curtain of cloud and stayed there for the
rest of the day, sulking until evening when there was a petulant
outburst of rain, a violent, intemperate shower which lasted
for no more than a minute or two.

I had not seen Brad all the long day. He had kept away from the tent whilst Mary was with me, and now that she had gone he had left me too—purposely, I suspect—alone with my little grief. And I would have had it so.

Inconsolable, I walked to the bushes where we had spent our earlier day, and, when the rain came on, took shelter under the thick hawthorn hedge.

As I stood there great grey clouds lumbered across the sky, carried on the breast of a strong wind which hurried through the elms, making those top-heavy trees writhe beneath the onslaught.

Whitethroats paused in their song to scold from their hiding-places in the hedgerow, and a pair of turtle-doves left the shelter of the nut bush to chase over the water, but the wind drifted them back again and they were content to sit crooning.

Dog-rose petals were shaken from the bushes in the flurry and lay in dingy clusters on the ground and on the water puddles; and the disorder looked so much like the untidy aftermath of a week-old wedding.

Grasses, in their whispering, bowed towards the east, and the gusty wind made this world of greenery look lighter in colour, for it turned the leaves of the meadow-sweet and hedge elder, nettle and cow parsnip, until only the pale underside of each blade was visible.

The floating water-lily leaves, too, were half raised from the water to fall back again and bounce about on the choppy wavelets like over-buoyant boats at anchor.

The greenfinch 'dreeped' monotonously as he swayed on a branch of may, but the blackbird still sang as though unaware of the greyness, seeming to know that this day was but one of summer's tantrums; and even as he sang a tinge of colour came to the sky on the evening horizon, and there was a mite of

promise of a fine tomorrow both in the heavens and in the birds' evensong; for now the willow-warbler sang again with the blackbird and the tumbling whitethroat, and the crooning doves snuggled together in the swaying elders.

The wind gusts ceased, and only a little whispering was left to the trees and to the tall grasses; and the rain began again, not hastily, in bad temper, but copiously, emptying the heart of the sky; weeping for a lost summer day, and ashamed of itself.

A GRUMBLE of thunder rumbled in the distance, and a wisp of wind hurried a clock of dandelion over the short-grazed grass.

A wink of lightning came from a hummock of grey cloud over the Tythorn hills and big fat drops of rain bounced on the yellow gravel towpath as Brad and I walked slowly to the stile by the canal bridge.

I glanced a little anxiously at the sky.

'What's the matter?' asked Brad sharply.

'Do you think we shall be all right?' I inquired. 'It looks a bit threatening.'

'Aw, that's all right! It'll pass!' he replied brusquely. 'There'll not be much rain.' To Brad the rain was the greater inconvenience, the storm was secondary. I have seen him sit happily in a shallow cave made in a meadow haystack, whistling untunefully but with never a care, in the most violent thunderstorm. He was sheltered from the rain and therefore content.

We heard no more of the thunder, and the sudden rain ceased as abruptly as it had started, leaving a few pock-holes in the dust of the ginger-coloured path.

Two boys, fishing for perch between the walls of the bridge, looked up at us as we approached the stile, but made no comment, and we climbed to a seat on the topmost rail.

For a long time we watched the red floats on the water, but they were very steady, swaying slightly to the slow run of the water but showing no sign of interested fish below.

The lads became fidgety. Brad had a disturbing habit of staring fixedly at a person, and I had also gained something of this idiosyncrasy from him. To most people this had a most irritating effect.

One of the boys changed the bait on his hook, taking from a round tin a pink wriggling worm which he affixed and cast into the water again, near to the dark walls on the opposite side of the canal.

Still the red float drifted gently downstream with nothing to indicate a bite, and the boy and his companion turned on us with flushed faces.

'What do you want?' demanded the taller of the two, a little temper showing in his voice. But Brad kept very calm.

'Nothing,' he replied mildly. I knew that, if pressed, he was more than a match for both, and they knew it too.

The questioner grunted.

For another half-hour we sat, and the top bar of the stile began to cut into the flesh of my rump, but I only shifted my position slightly. Brad gazed wonderingly at the red floats and the boys grew more furious each minute, murmuring angrily about fools who sat and watched, and cursing all striped fish that ever swam in the canal, until at last the strain became too much for them. Suddenly one of them turned to Brad and offered him rod and line.

'Do you want to have a go?' he almost shouted. 'You come on then! You, sitting there watching!' But Brad shook his head and declined the offer and settled to a more comfortable position to continue the staring.

This was too much for the young fishermen. With an oath the taller boy pulled out his line, reeled in the silk and folded his rod, and the younger one did the same.

As they packed their traps they damned and blasted all fish that would not bite on a thundery day, and stormed away along the footpath.

'You've forgotten your bait,' Brad called after them, and they came back again and kicked the round tins of worms into the canal, and by the way they looked at Brad they would dearly have liked to serve him the same way. But he sat still, there on the stile, watching the wriggling bait slowly sink to the bottom of the cut.

Suddenly he chuckled. A lovely striped fish, a really good perch, oozed out of the blackness of the underwater walls and gently sucked down one of the discarded worms.

A few more fishes came from the darkness and soon all the bait was gone.

The watching fishermen turned and went silently on their way. But we stayed on a while longer; we had nothing better to do, and the day was warm and fresher now that the little storm had passed.

There was a movement on the towpath, a shiver of grass-heads on the hedgebank, and a wedge of fawn poked between the stems of keck.

I murmured softly to Brad and, slowly turning our heads, we saw the stoat as it came jerkily down the pathway. It travelled only a few yards before disappearing again in the grass, and we watched closely for its reappearance.

'Wonder what he's after,' whispered Brad. 'A nice thing if

there's going to be many of them about. There'll be no rabbits!'

I did not answer, for, truth to tell, I much preferred the sleek beauty of the cream-breasted stoat to all the rabbits of the field. They held a strange fascination for me, with their wonderful purposefulness, their tenacity, so directly opposed to my own rather unstable life.

I loved their savagery, the way they killed their meat and then ate like aristocrats, drinking the red wine of their victims, rejecting the offal; and conies were offal, fit only for the carrion crow and our hungry family.

The stoat would not eat them, only the brains and a few of the choicer tit-bits, but it would lick the blood.

The fox would make a meal from them of course, but then he would eat rats too, and beetles and almost anything else. He would kill the gone-wild cat and devour it as though it were the choicest morsel, or lick into his chops the ring-dove squab, fresh fallen from its nest in the elm poles above.

I liked the stoat, bloody and fastidious.

The cocksfoot grass trembled again and the stoat stood on tiptoe looking out inquisitively over the shorter bents and, as we kept quite still, it came out on to the path and ran over the trodden ground.

When it came to the stile upon which we now leaned (the sharp edge of the topmost rail had won the battle with my behind) it paused and snarled in anger and alarm as it caught our scent.

For a moment I thought that it would vanish again in the hedgerow, but instead it danced a few crazy steps on the pathway in front of us, then stood on its hind legs and spat and made a sharp sound, a savage little threat—'C-heck-a'—as though sneezing.

Still we did not move. We half closed our eyes and watched

through squinted slits—wobbling eyes terrify most wild things—and soon, inquisitively, the dog stoat came to our feet, scenting and snarling, daring a little, racing back again to the gravel walk.

For several minutes he kept up the game until, satisfied that we were no more than part and parcel of the stile, he ran sinuously under the bridge and out of sight. But not for long. As soon as he had gone Brad walked softly forward and watched the animal's progress down the canal side, and I joined him.

The stoat was on the food hunt; this much was obvious, for, every few yards, he lifted his head and smelled the warm air. He faltered at a timothy tussock on the bankside and sniffed. Slowly he urged his body round the tuft of grass until his head was poised above the water, and suddenly there was a subdued splash as a frantic water-vole saw the hunter above him and hastily dived for shelter.

But his escape was short lived. The sleek stoat swung round acrobatically and disappeared into a bank hole a foot above the water line; and in the darkness of underground he must have met the vole head on, for, in a while, there was a trace of red stain on the water to mix with the ribbon of buff mud that the water-vole had stirred up, and we guessed that the little animal had lived its day.

We waited patiently, watching that part of the bank where the stoat had disappeared, and soon the wedge-face peered above the patch of red-nettle and woundwort, and there was a smear of blood on his breast, seen as he stood a-tiptoe, looking out cautiously along the towpath.

His savage little eyes fixed on us as we spied on him from under the arch of the bridge, and he curled back his chops and showed his teeth in an angry snarl, but we remained frozen still and, his anxiety appeased for the moment, he came jerkily out on to the pathway.

As he approached the bridge we retreated carefully out of sight, taking up a position again by the stile, waiting for the hunter as he came under the bridge bow.

'He's got a mouth full of something,' I remarked softly.

'Course he has!' retorted Brad. 'Ain't he just killed a water-rat?'

'But', I protested, 'why should he carry it? Why doesn't he feed where he caught it?'

My brother scratched his head in thought but made no further answer.

Our conversation had been carried on in a whisper, for we knew that the stoat was nearing the bridge, and yet we did not realize how near until we heard a muffled 'Chek-a, chek-a', almost at our feet.

There was the dog stoat, his face almost hidden by the severed hind leg of the water-vole which he was carrying. He had halted exactly where we had stood on the towpath watching the kill, and beyond that point he would not go, but danced madly around, the bloody leg still in his mouth, as though there was some tangible barrier in his way.

Suddenly he caught sight of us standing there, and we creased our faces and watched again through the slits of our eyelids; but even so he became afraid now. The prize dropped from his mouth on the yellow gravel and the stoat ran away from it, down the path, out of sight below the bridge, but we knew that he would come back for the meat.

From nowhere it seemed a second stoat appeared as if by magic from the opposite direction taken by the first, and now this smaller gill stoat moved quickly down the path towards the vole leg discarded by her mate.

She paused for a moment when she saw us by the stile, and chattered in alarm, and at the sound of her chickering the male came hurrying forward again towards the discarded leg.

For a while they looked at each other across the invisible scent barrier of our earlier standing, then went into a crazy dance, a kind of wild ritual performance, as though exorcising a devil, after which they ignored us and our foot scents.

There was a show of petulance and a little snarling quarrel as they both approached the vole leg, but in the end, after a bit of tug-of-war, the gill gained the prize and carried it back along the way she had come, whilst the dog stoat went over the tow-path to the bank hole in which he had killed his game.

We watched the gill disappear in the long grasses of the hedgeside, and then Brad ran on tiptoes to the spot where he had last seen her. He beckoned to me, and when I got to his side he pointed over the hedge towards a small stream that wound through the open field, a tiny brooklet a yard wide— no more—by the side of which we often passed the time of the sunny days watching the red-breasted sticklebacks on nest guard in the deeper pools.

'She went up the side of the hedge,' Brad explained. 'Right up to that ash fence.' He pointed. 'Then she cut across the corner and went to that dead willow. She's got young 'uns. I tell you, boyo!'

I looked in the direction which he had indicated. By the side of the stream, on the bank, stood a stumpy willow tree, a pollarded trunk which had once thrown out a few straight branches from its tip, but now, for some reason or other, the tree had died after giving so little of life.

It is not an uncommon sight to see a line of such small trees by the side of meadow streams, and almost always they are pollarded willows. There appears to be a certain symmetry in their setting too, which is sometimes a little puzzling, but there is no mystery about their growth.

In most cases the trees were placed there merely as posts to hold the fencing wire which prevented the thirsty cattle treading down the banks of the stream in their desire for water, and induced them to use the more regular watering places lower down the brook. If cattle are permitted to use the higher water at will the water in the lower drinks becomes foul and contaminated. The posts were there to prevent this.

In other cases the brook formed the boundary of a man's land, and the wire fence was erected to mark the bounds and to enclose the stock.

But willow posts have a way of rooting quickly, especially when set near water, and within a few years the wiring posts take root. From the several tips a spark of life is pointed to the sun and, in so short a time, the tiny brooklet is willow-lined and lovelier.

As the years pass the need for the fencing wire ceases to exist, the wire decays and many of the casually rooted willows are hacked down. But often one or two will be retained to act as rubbing posts for the cattle or shade spots for the sheep.

'Here she comes!' whispered Brad. My eyes had not left the base of the dead willow, but yet I could not see the female stoat.

'Down by the hedge, there!' Brad murmured. 'In the nettle clump. Watch her come round by the thorns!'

Sure enough the little wedge face looked inquiringly out over the meadow, making sure that the way was clear before racing, back-a-hump, towards us.

Carefully we drew away from our hide, away from the path which she had taken on her last journey, and as we did so my brother uttered a surprised cry. There, almost at our feet, was the male, his teeth showing in an angry snarl, looking at us with hatred in his little eyes. Just for a moment we saw him, then, in a flash, he vanished in the trash of the hedgerow, gone as though he had been wiped clean off the earth; neither sight nor faint sound left to show where he had gone nor where going.

Brad beckoned to me and we walked back to the stile.

'We'll wait here,' he said. 'I reckon the old dog stoat has had his feed in the hole, but the bitch'll come for more for her babbies. She'll carry the lot away, you see!' And he was right. We stood by the fence until the day grew late, watching the lithe little animal carry the ghastly carcass of the water-vole bit by bit under the bridge and along the gravel path to her home by the brook.

We did not, however, see the dog stoat again; the gill was left on her own to the task.

After the third or fourth journey, both my brother and I began to get fidgety, for she seemed to be much longer at the vole-hole.

'Funny!' said Brad. 'Wonder what she's up to.'

'Perhaps gone a different way,' I hazarded. 'She should be here by now.'

Brad shook his head, puzzled, and I began to think of leaving. We had been beside that stile for the whole of the evening and, as the stoat appeared to have gone, I could see no point in our remaining.

Through the thinner places in the scrawny hawthorn I could see, in the gathering twilight, the white outline of my tent in the four-acre, and I wished to be there. I also heard the squeaky gate—rusty on its hinges—creak as the first of the giggling couples came slowly over the Wranglands pasture towards the bridge beside which we were standing.

'Come on!' I urged. 'Let's go!'

Brad agreed, but, as an afterthought, took a step or two to the bridge arch and peered down the towpath. Instantly he drew back and pressed himself against the upright brickwork. Under the bridge, staggering under her load, struggled the

D

little stoat, the huge, bloody head of the water-vole in her
mouth.

Her head was held high so that her burden was clear of the
ground, and she walked sideways, crabwise, for the load
obscured her forward view. As she struggled along she tripped
from time to time on the streamers of the vole's intestines
which dragged along the ground under her body, but, in-
exorably, she went her way, a wonderfully fierce little
creature, all savage.

After she had passed under the bridge span she dropped the
head on the grass by the side of the towpath and licked the
blood from her lips and from the stained white of her belly.

For a moment I thought she would abandon her task, for
she left it there lying where it had fallen, and ran a few steps
up the pathway. She raised herself on her hind legs and turned
her head aside as though listening; and suddenly she screamed,
a high-pitched chatter, 'Chicker, chicker, chicker, chicker,' and
waited expectantly for an answer.

But there was no reply to her calling, and she went back
again and danced ecstatically round the messy head, pouncing
abruptly upon it, half carrying, half dragging it away into the
hedge-stoles, out of our sight now that the light had become
so dim.

Brad and I parted at the hand gate by the canal side, he going
to the dull red lights of the village, I to my quiet tent.

'We'll take a look at that old willow tomorrow,' he said as
we walked away from each other.

'Tomorrow, y' know, we'll find the nest!' He raised his
voice a little to carry over the distance of our separation. 'I'd
like a young 'un to tame!'

WE FOUND the nest, or at least the place under the willow where it had been, but the young were no longer there and Brad swore.

'But they must ha' been there last night!' he almost yelled. 'Didn't we see the gill taking food to them?'

'Must ha' been ready for leaving the nest even then,' I reasoned. 'Must ha' been pretty big to eat that sort of food. Little 'uns would still suckle,' and Brad snorted, but I stuck to my point, for I believed that I was right.

'Fat lot o' good that is, talking like that!' he grumbled. 'It won't help me to catch one to train, will it?'

I was scornful.

'You couldn't tame a stoat!' I retorted. 'You! Tame a stoat! Why, they're beyond taming! It wouldn't be right!'

I hated the thought of such a wild creature coming under the dulling influence of a human being. But Brad was argumentative. He'd show me whether he couldn't tame a stoat. He'd tamed many a bird, and birds were the more difficult.

His voice trailed off into a silence, and my eyes followed his stare. In a flash we were flat on the ground, our heads raised only a little above the bents in order that we might see a bare patch of earth which the shading cattle had worn under the wide-limbed elm that grew in the quick-set hedge.

'Gosh!' I exclaimed. 'Look at that!' But I might have been speaking to myself for all the notice that Brad took.

He, like me, was looking at four young stoats playing a crazy game of tig on the trodden patch, a mad chasing game of twists and turns that bewildered the eyes.

The young had not the sleek appearance of their parents, for much of the baby fur still clung to them, especially about the face, but in agility they were as adept as anything I have ever seen. Their antics were completely wild; the most wonderful acrobatics.

Once the parent (it was the gill) came from the hedgerow to join in the fun, but there was more in her participation than play, for she stalked the largest of the four young, crouching low to the ground, weaving swiftly from side to side in front of him on the bare patch of earth, suddenly springing at him, taking him behind the head and dragging him towards the hedge-stoles.

When she released him again he flew at her in terrible anger, chickering mardily, but she sent him whining with a sharp nip over the nose, and after a little pause the four youngsters went on with the fantastic game again just as before, except that a little of the lesson which the mother had taught seemed to creep into it, a smaller stoat bounding about in front of one of the others, trying to get a purchase on its neck, persisting even after taking a bit of a thrashing.

We watched them for some minutes, and I would have been content to watch them for the rest of the day, but Brad had other ideas.

He pointed to a gap in the hedge fifty yards from the stoat family and indicated that he wished me to go through the gap to the other side of the hedge, thus placing the stoats between the pair of us.

We had often done this before when hunting the bush-roosting water-hens at the close of the year.

Many creatures become a little bemused when they find themselves sandwiched between two groups of hunters.

I crawled along the furrows of the field until I was far enough away for the playing animals not to see me, then through the gap and into the adjacent field, giving Brad a waved signal when I had taken up a position directly opposite to him.

Slowly we rose from the ground and closed in on the unsuspecting stoats. At first they continued with their game and I felt sure that we might be lucky enough to capture one, but a waft of scent must have reached the dam, for suddenly she gave an abrupt 'Kik' and all action ceased. Another slight call from her and the young disappeared as if by magic.

We searched the hedge-bank, the weeds and the haw-stoles for almost an hour but found nothing of them.

We looked up into the higher branches, hoping that they had taken refuge there. Brad found the dead-end nest-hole of a rabbit and spent a tiring time ripping up the turf like a mole, but when he came to the end of the tunnel there was nothing but a little soft fur where the baby conies had been born, and a few of their early droppings matted together.

Tired and disheartened, we gave up the hunt. I grinned at Brad and he laughed ruefully.

'I'll perhaps get one yet, one day,' he said.

But I shook my head in disbelief and chided him. 'You! Tame a stoat! Wor!'

NO MATTER how hot the day it was always cool in the shade of the billowy hawthorn bushes that grew on the canal bank near to the tunnel. They reared up in tiers along the whole length of the slope, some pink in their blossom, some red, but most of them white; and the profusion of the flowers made the air rank and heavy and yet very pleasing.

I could lie in the perfume of the may and come to no harm, but the elder bushes by the brookside were bad bedfellows. Their scent was also rank and heavy, but it had a thieving quality which took away the senses and brought on a dull drowsiness, and finally sleep.

'Ne'er doze i' the scent of the eld,' old Sophy, the Romany,

48

used to warn. 'You'll get bad heads and a slow awakening,' and she was right.

Narrow cattle-walks led down the steep bank to the water, and the clumsy animals would run awkwardly downhill for a few yards as though in play, gleefully going to their drink, skidding to a halt in the sedges and struggling laboriously upwards again to the pasture land beyond the hill after their thirst had been quenched.

There were many snakes in the cool dampness under the haw bushes, all harmless grass-snakes, yellow-collared and stinky; and, because of their presence, few people came to the bank in summer time, for they had an abhorrence of the reptiles. That was one of the delights of the place—the absence of others.

Sometimes towards evening, at the time when the shafts of sunlight had almost gone from the ground and the shadows of the ant-hills had lengthened so far that they had disappeared altogether, then would the farmer's dog come to join me for a while, his work done until tomorrow's daybreak. But he would not stay long, just for time to sniff at the tall thistle and to carefully leave his own scent there; to search feverishly over the shorter grass where the sun sat each day, seeking some strange attraction on a pad of bare ground and, having found it, rolling his legs in the air for several moments, pausing only to smell again at the unobservable lure as though to refresh his memory.

In a while a shrill whistle would echo over the fields, and Rover, tail down, would steal dejectedly away to answer his master's summons.

It was on a fine hot afternoon that my brother came to me at the bushes. I had lain there in the shade and the scent, listening to the fussing water-hens as they fidgeted with their newly hatched young, little black bobbles less than a day old and yet water-borne and agile.

I heard the footfalls on the ground long before Brad was near, the heavier thud as he leaped over the stile and the kiss of the grass as he walked on the sward.

'Hallo!' he said, and sat on a hillock facing me. 'Gor! It's hot!'

I agreed, and warned him of the ant-hill. He sat for some time without saying more, throwing a few sun-baked rabbit droppings at the toe of his boot, not purposefully but mechanically, almost subconsciously as though his thoughts were elsewhere.

After he had exhausted his supply of pellets he rose abruptly, and for a moment I thought my warning regarding the ants had been too late.

'I say!' he began, 'this is a rare place. A snake!' He pointed to one of the smaller bushes. 'Under there! I saw it slither in.' He shuddered. 'Aw! don't stop here! It's a poor place. Let's go up'ards to the Green Lane. There's peewits' eggs in the ploughland there.'

I knew of the nests in the Pensfield and the implication in my brother's invitation. We had plenty of customers for these delicacies, and the prospect of making a little pocket-money was not to be too lightly dismissed. But I was comfortable in the cool of the bushes and ignored the suggestion.

'Wonder what snakes were made for,' Brad ruminated. 'Don't seem to be much use to anyone.'

I made no reply nor, I think, did he expect me to.

He went on: 'Nub'dy keeps 'em as pets I shouldn't think! Wonder what they're made for. Eh! Boyo!' he burst out. 'Who'd want snakes?'

Appealed to thus I answered sleepily: 'Museums, I suppose.'

For a while nothing more was said, and I thought he had forgotten the subject. The white-backed bees were on the clovers that grew in the sun patches, and their greed spun a little scent in the air, so slight that it was scarcely perceptible in the heavier perfume of the may.

It was good to lie there with nothing better to do than laze and listen to the white-backed bees; waiting for each to come to the nearer clover head; hearing them out of earshot as they travelled away over the hill.

Brad's grumbling voice mixed in with the humming of the bees until, sleepily, I could scarcely distinguish one from the other.

'Who'd want them? What good are they?'

Suddenly I felt a tug at my shirt sleeve.

'Boyo!' whispered Brad urgently. 'Boyo! It's coming out again. Gor! It's a whopper! Hey! Boyo!'

I woke with a start.

'What's up!' I cried, a little dazed.

'The snake! It's coming out of that bush. Look!'

I turned in the direction indicated by his pointing finger and saw a fine specimen of a grass-snake, clean in its new coat, all green and gold.

Brad clutched my arm as I moved towards it, and would have held me back.

'It's all right,' I assured him. 'It'll not hurt! It's harmless enough, you idiot!' But he was unconvinced.

In the slight scuffle the snake took fright again and dived for the stoles of the haw bush, and by the time I had disentangled myself from Brad's grip it had disappeared, and I was not sufficiently interested to prise the reptile from its burrow.

'They're mucky things,' said Brad, pulling a wry face. 'Who'd want them things?' He paused as though struck by a sudden thought.

'I say! Did you say that the museums keep these things? Where do they get them from?'

I said I didn't know. From the country I supposed.

'Aye, and they'd have to pay for 'em too,' replied my brother. 'They'd pay a fair price, I'll bet!'

I demurred, but Brad was insistent.

'You come on! You get up! No telling what we'd get for a big 'un.'

My brother saw a fortune in most things, a fortune in pocket-money, anyway. He talked to me as we sat on the cool ground, planning the capture of such a harmless thing as though it were a deadly cobra.

'We'll cut a snake-stick apiece,' he said. 'A long 'un.'

I assured him that it was quite unnecessary, they could be more easily taken by hand, a suggestion which made him shudder again. I think that snakes of any kind were the only creatures of which Brad was afraid.

'You do the catching, then,' he replied as though granting me a favour. 'You catch 'em. I'll stand by with the snake-stick, just in case.'

It was arranged—by him of course—that we should keep the reptile captive in the garden of our house throughout the night, delivering it in the morning to the museum nine miles away.

'We'll ha' to walk,' he said, and I grimaced. Not that I minded the tramp to the town, for it was through very pleasant country most of the way. It was to the town itself that I objected; it overawed me. There were so many people in that lonely forest of tall buildings that I became panic-stricken lest I might become so easily lost there and never find a way back to the meadows.

'You'll have to sleep at home tonight. We must start early in the morning.'

I pulled a face again. Brad's suggestion that I should, once again, revert to the stuffiness of a cottage bedroom appalled me.

'Only for a night, just one night,' he pleaded. 'That'll not

hurt you. You'll not be up in time otherwise. You see, we
must start early.'

In spite of my protests Brad was adamant.

'You'll sleep at home, just for the one night. Gor, boyo!
You think! We'll get no end for a big 'un. Museums are rich
people!'

The lure of money, added to my brother's reasoning, duly
persuaded me and I succumbed.

In spite of my protests Brad cut a V-ended snake-stick
from a blackthorn bush and trimmed the thorns from it, and
whilst he was thus engaged I went to the hawthorn clump
under which the large snake had taken refuge.

There was an accumulation of old rotted leaves to be cleared
away before I could reach the stoles of the shrub, and it was
some little while before I found the quarry.

By the time my brother had come up to me I had discovered
the snake, hidden half in half out of a burrow which led under
the thick root arms. To extract the reptile I had to use a certain
amount of force, and this rather rough treatment both in-
furiated and frightened it. It hissed angrily when we had it in
the open. It struck several times at my hand when I tried to get
a better hold of it, and this threatening attitude completely
dumbfounded Brad, who would have gladly given up the
venture, but, seeing that no harm had come to me from this
feigned attack, he became a little more bold, and approached
the reptile again.

Soon it wound itself around my arm and its frantic struggles
ceased. A faint smell arose from it and grew stronger and
stronger until it became almost unendurable. The rough
handling and the fright of capture had induced the snake to
release a liquid from its tail end, and this was the cause of the
dreadful stench.

The brown of my bare arm was stained by a slightly darker

brown moisture, and, for a moment, I was so revolted by the
stink that I almost released the now placid reptile.

'Phew!' gasped Brad, and retched until he was a little sick
on the grass.

'Gor! What the devil is it? Phew! It ain't natural! Let it
go, for heaven's sake! It'll poison us both.'

But it was such a fine specimen, about three and a half feet
long, and so beautifully marked, all green and gold.

And now it lay quietly twined round my arm, its wedge-
shaped head held firmly between my finger and thumb and its
forked tongue stabbing out between its almost closed jaws,
searching and probing, like a divining rod; all anger and fright
gone now, and only the stink remaining.

I washed the snake in the canal; when the reptile felt the cool
water it struggled a little and uncoiled itself, but soon it lay again
in seeming content, and the air was fresher for the ablutions.

We took it over the fields, and in our journey the warmth of
the sun and the warmth of my arm brought to it a kind of
torpor. Now it would allow itself to be unwound from its rest
on my arm and permit us to handle it without treating us to a
further dose of the obnoxious smell.

As a precaution I placed it in my pocket when we approached
the village, for the people there were as averse to these creatures
as Brad had been, but their ignorance of their habits was even
greater than his.

They believed that the black tongues were stings, poison
barbs that killed, and they were terrified of them. In consequence many of the quite harmless things were destroyed for
possessing a member which was, in many cases, less of a danger
than that of their murderers.

A few dogs followed us up the hill to our home, sniffing
inquisitively, nose in the air, uncertain of the stink; but Brad
pelted them with road flints until they went away.

When my mother saw the snake she recoiled a little but said nothing. She had been well weathered in a hard school and had nerves tough as whit-leather.

We assured her that we wished to lodge the snake in the garden only for the night, afterwards we would deliver it up to the museum.

She watched us as we put it into a wooden box in the shrubbery, and even helped us to secure the lid with two large brick-bats, but I could tell that she was far from easy. At some time during the evening, however, her uneasiness vanished as if by magic, and I am sure that she slept peacefully through the night; unlike myself, who found a stifle of house-room after the freshness of my tent.

Brad and I were up early the next day to prepare for our long journey to town. But when we went to collect the snake we found the lid of the imprisoning box had been moved slightly, allowing a space between top and side. It was obviously through this gap that the snake and escaped, and although we searched high and low there was no trace of the reptile. It had made a clean getaway.

And as we stood looking dejectedly at the empty box my mother approached. She listened patiently as we told of our tragedy and sympathized with us.

'Must ha' been that old ginger tom cat,' she murmured.

But when I recall her many journeys into the garden during that previous night, and her sudden regain of ease, I doubt if it was the tom.

But she had slept well in the peace of the night when there had been no peace before.

Most of the village folk were afraid of snakes, and for no reason. Many simply could not stand the sight of the reptiles, and shuddered even at the thought of them.

Men killed whenever they saw them, using long sticks to

batter away life, and when I protested they cuffed my ears and told me to clear off. Often, in revenge, I would take a newly caught specimen from my pocket and display it to them, walking slowly towards them with the snake coiled around my outstretched arm.

Then they would back away in alarm, threatening me with dire punishment if I didn't 'take the damned thing away'.

'Look at the young fool,' they would warn. And I, to add to their discomfort, would allow the probing tongue to touch my cheek and lips, flaunting their fears.

Yet oddly enough there was an old gentleman in the village who, though as scared of the reptiles as the rest, had the strange hobby of collecting the sloughs, the discarded over-skins of the snakes.

He would not gather them himself, for he confessed to me his antipathy, but asked me to deliver to him any that I should find in the haw bushes.

I was curious to know for what purpose he required them, but he would not tell me.

'Never you mind!' he said. 'You just get them for me.'

We agreed on a price for each slough, and thereupon throughout the summer I made a little more pocket-money out of the transaction.

I had an idea that the supply position could be increased by using other methods too, and, when I found a dead, battered creature lying on the hawthorn hedge where it had been slung by its murderers, I carefully peeled off the skin and took it to the old man, hoping that it would be even more acceptable than the flimsy colourless slough.

He gave one look at it, turned pale, and retched.

'Take it away!' he gasped. 'Take the stinking thing away! What a dreadful thing!'

I could never understand why he should have wanted the

sloughs in preference to the finely marked skins; but that was his business; he paid me well for what he wanted.

My brother and I collected for other people of the village too. The schoolmaster—who was an enthusiastic shot, although not a very good one—wanted information about the partridges' nests that we found in our wanderings, especially on the ground over which he rented the shooting rights, but all this had to be supplied gratis, neither we expecting, nor he proffering, reward.

Sometimes we picked up a few sticks from the hedge bottom for old blind Fossy Grain, who lived alone in a pudding-bag lane at the end of the village, and as we kicked open the door of his little cottage he would swear violently and shamble towards us.

'Brought you a bit of firewood, Fossy,' Brad would announce, dropping the load in the black fireplace.

Fossy gave us nothing for our trouble, for he had nothing to give, being almost completely poverty stricken. It was in fact his poverty, not his affliction, that made such an impression on Brad.

'He's poor, you see!' was his excuse for anything that he did to help Fossy, who showed little gratitude.

I often wondered why we took the trouble to help the old man; no one else in the village would go near him, but Brad always had the answer.

'He's poor, you see, boyo! That's why!'

THE FRUITS of the field went to my mother. We gathered mushrooms, pounds and pounds of them, in our big deep willow baskets.

Long before birdsong, before the sun rose from behind Moss meadows, Brad and I were out in the sheep fields picking the hour-old fungi from the fairy rings in the grazing lands.

It was of no use to wait until daybreak, for at that hour every jobless male in the village would be there, grumbling because they were too late. No! We went before the mist had lifted, before the cowman had left his foot-trail in the wet grass on his way to call the herd to their milking.

Brad had tapped on my tent wall and thrust a basket into my hand, and we had gone to the mushroom field before the cowman's 'Cup-on! Cup-on, then!' had sounded over the countryside.

We frequently fell into an argument with an occasional moucher—a townee street-seller—who disputed our right to be there, but generally we kept well out of the way of such people.

When, later in the morning, we took our harvest home Mother spread them out on the floor in the large dairy, sorting the various kinds into their respective heaps.

There were customers for all of them, and she knew to which house they would be sent. The small pink-gilled mushrooms, which we called springers, went to the wife of the farmer from whose field we had earlier gathered them. She paid a good price for these luxuries, but not the greater price of losing her man so early in the morning.

The larger 'platers' were sold to other housewives of the village who cooked them with the breakfast bacon; and the squat, unopened 'buttons' were cooked in meat pies or cleaned and wrapped in suet dumplings.

All the mushrooms were carefully sorted and placed—gills

uppermost—on the spotless thralls of the dairy, the springers in their place, the platers—dark-gilled and a little smelly—in theirs, and the buttons in a corner by themselves.

There was one other type that we gathered in quantities, the big bulbous horse-mushrooms which we often found in the large tussocks of grass. They were not much use for eating, being tough and rather tasteless, but made the most excellent ketchup, and because of this were very welcome, for my mother made a good deal of money from them.

She used four or five big earthenware panshins in the preparation of the liquid, and throughout the summer it was always possible to see at least one of these containers full of ketchup at one or other stage of development.

It was not a difficult process. The mushrooms—or flops— were broken up and placed at the bottom of the earthenware panshins and covered with a sprinkling of salt. Further layers of mushrooms and salt were added alternately until the containers were full. After standing for a certain time the whole was thoroughly stirred each day, then strained and boiled, spiced and bottled.

There were many local recipes for making ketchup, but my mother seemed to possess one with special qualities, for her preparation was always in great demand; so much so that we rarely tasted it.

We went to the blackthorn fox coverts and brought home skepsful of sloes to be made into sloe gin; and to the valley hedges where the pink crab-apples grew, and these were made into the lovely semi-transparent crab jelly, so favoured by the folk who loved good food.

We collected elderberries from the hedges nearer home, and from these was obtained a light wine. Earlier in the year we had gathered the elder flowers for the same purpose, but this innocuous-looking beverage was not to be trusted. I have

E

seen many a hard-drinking man lose his legs after partaking of
no more than a tumblerful.

There was something wonderfully rich about my mother's
dairy, for the food found there was reminiscent of olden,
more vernal, days. In the spring there was the scent of the
cowslips drying on the thralls, the sun of early golden meadows
waiting to be turned by subtle alchemy into wine.

Later the purple elderberries lay there, waiting their turn.

In summer the mushrooms and the stinky ketchup. In early
autumn a brace of partridges hung from the hooks in the white
ceiling, a long-tailed pheasant, the pink half-head of pig's face,
newly chauled; all good things destined for some house or
other in the village.

There were naked rabbits which Brad and I had caught,
and they were for our eating.

'We must make shift with them for a while,' said Mother
when we looked at the fleshy objects with no liking.

We had learned something of the ritual of the gentleman's
pantry too. We knew that whereas a rabbit must be skinned
and gutted as soon after capture as possible, a hare should
hang in his coat and with his innards undrawn.

'There's a smell!' Brad would say. 'Such a smell!'

'Oh, it's the game!' he was told. 'It must be well hung or
Mr Wilkerton will think it tough!'

In the capacious cellar went the home-made wines—parsnip,
elder, cowslip—all to be sold later. A shaft of sunlight peeping
through the iron rails of the window touched some of the
bottles and lit them up in their colours; fell on some of the
yellow frogs too that abounded in the damp half-dark of below
ground, and reflected unnaturally from the wet skin of their
bodies.

The bottles lay on their sides like sleeping children in a
slum, glad of the little light coming in from the outside world,

and the cobwebs hung like curtains over them; ragged gowns, all witchy in the gloom.

The damned lived in that cellar among the spider-webs; all the ghosts of a million meadow flowers, the will-o'-the-wisps of the summer days, imprisoned there among the frogs; all the opposites of the chink of light that peeped surreptitiously in at the window.

I hated that cellar. There was nothing like it in all my small experience of life. When I was very infrequently sent to fetch a bottle of wine the command was always accompanied by the injunction:

'And make haste! Don't stay down there!'

Neither Brad nor my parents understood the reason for my delay in the cellar, and I dared not tell them for fear of their displeasure and Brad's scorn.

There was a strange influence in that dark place which I felt immediately my feet reached the bottom of the stone steps. All life seemed to ebb from me as I walked over the cold floor, as though it were being stolen from me and I too numbed to care.

I know that I always stayed quietly, without moving, for an age in the very centre of the room, scarcely breathing, unable to break the spell of inaction which bound me; seeing with mesmerized eyes the strand of spider silk swaying in the sunbeam; forgetful of my errand until I heard Brad's voice at the cellar door.

'Boyo! Hurry up! What are you doing down there? Come up at once!'

Then, with a start, I would wake to reality again and race up the stone stairs as if all the ghosts of the underworld were after me.

Such visits to the dread cellar were few, for little of my life was spent at home. The lure of the fields was overwhelming in all seasons, but at no time more than when there was a sniff of mown hay in the nostrils.

Of course a little sadness came after hay-making, for then the birds went dozy and forgot to sing, but even their silence was in keeping with the warm scented days of July when the sun made all things lazy. And hardly had the hay smell left the countryside than the brown wheat was down, and then there was a little more vigour in the world. Birds came back into song and men called to their horses and to one another.

Brad and I had leaned on the long stile watching them at work until evening, and, when the day's work was done and the lathering horses relieved of their gear, we climbed from the fence and went across the meadows to the four-acre.

There we sat, as was usual, into the twilight; myself with head cupped in my hands; Brad planning ahead, plotting how best to take the hare that had its run in the small plough strip of Longleas.

'If we set a wire . . .' Brad's voice trailed into indecision. He did not expect an answer.

'It'll come round by the brook, crossing there.' He indicated the trail of the hare with a piece of stick on the flat top of a half-dried cow-pat.

'Then uphill to there. Funny thing about a hare! It'll always run better uphill, y' know. Falls over itself when it runs downhill! Back legs too long! They trip him up!'

He rambled on disjointedly, explaining, suggesting.

'I'll fix the wire. You walk over the plough. He'll go for the gap. Then we'll have him. Gor! They do scream when they're caught!'

He rose to go.

'We'll perhaps do that tomorrow, eh?'

'It depends on the hare,' I answered. 'He'll most likely not be there.'

'I'll come with you to the gate,' I suggested, but he shook his head.

'I'm not going straight home,' he explained. 'You see, I put a wire in down by the blackthorns. Think I'll just have a look at that before I turn in.'

'I'll come too!' I replied, and he raised no objection.

We went in silence to the gap in the sloe bushes. There was a trace of dew on the grass which polished the muck from the toes of our boots; and the mist began to rise among the distant group of trees, not as it did in the spring when a wisp of white cloud seesawed up and down the scrawny trunks, a wide band of gossamer; but this evening the curtain was dingy grey, murky, first covering the feet of the giants, then creeping insidiously upwards like a reaching hand, obliterating the lower branches and making the roosting doves ball their feathers and croodle closer to each other.

There was no prisoner in Brad's snare. Out of the corner of my eye I saw a dark shape skulking along a furrow of the pasture land strip, and a wandering dog, black as night, paused and crouched as he saw us at the thorns, but soon he passed on about his business, leaving us to ours.

Brad pulled from the ground the holding peg and wrapped up the snare.

'You're not leaving it for the night, then?' I queried.

'Not much with that about,' he answered wryly, indicating the disappearing dog. 'He'll take all that the wire gets.'

I nodded in agreement, and we turned away from the small spinney.

Brad took a short cut over the hedge to the village, leaving me to a long walk back to my tent; but that is what I would have wished, for I loved the evenings, even though the slight damp brought on a little irritation in my throat.

The ground stood higher in the four-acre and there was

rarely trouble there, but here, in the lower fields where the water lay after thunder rain, a dankness seemed to cling to all things at the end of the day.

The blackbirds—not yet at roost—made a racket from the hedges as I walked slowly by, and the midget wren creeled, and suddenly the fields became alive with noise.

From farther down the hedgerow more yittering blackbirds fled along the ditchways, disturbing the peace of the meadows, and causing the creaking partridges to call the louder; and all because of a black dog wandering, and I wandering too; all this fuss in the misty evening.

I walked over the field to an untidy gap in the hedge to where the quickset joined a rotted lichen-clad gatepost.

Some time earlier I had put a loop of wire at such and such a place within the gap; a running loop, a cunning loop, a care-adjusted snare, which now held a struggling rabbit.

How the trapped animal had escaped the notice of the mouching dog I could not understand, but, thanking the stars for my good fortune, I took the frantic rabbit from the run of the loop and gently pressed out its knotty neck.

It felt heavy as it died in my hands, and the fear went from its eyes and only wonder remained for a second before the grey film obliterated all.

That much is true of all the rabbits that I have known; other animals pass away differently.

The stoat and the weasel die with a wonderful hatred showing in their eyes, a life-long savagery intensified when they see life slipping away.

The hare has terror showing there, a wild, stark terror that appals as much as the last dying shriek which is so upsetting.

I have seen foxes die too, but when they are pulled down there seems to be a far-away look about them; their gaze is fixed not on the hound that dispatches them, but on some distant place, far beyond our sight. The baleful fox passes on, contemptuous of earth.

A rat dies afraid and a vole surprised, his little bright eyes asking questions to the last.

But a bird dies in peace, as though its soul had wings and were glad to be gone, and yet the little that is left becomes a saddening thing, a stringy neck and a few crumpled feathers; no more than a half a dozen pennyweights.

I pressed the juices from the body of the rabbit and tucked it in the crook of my arm. A little owl cried from the low branch of the hillside elm, and another answered from the willows down the vale, chiding me for my misdeed, but soon there was quiet among the daylight birds, no sound from any of them now; no magpies chattered, the wren creeled no more and the blackbirds ceased their warning.

The dingy mist had collected into a long narrow band which climbed almost to the tree tops and stayed there, trapped in the leaf domes; and above it hung an impersonal lemon half-moon, limpid and aloof. As I walked with my prize over Wranglands towards my tent I became aware of a dark shadow in the distance, and the black dog came stealthily towards me, stalking me over the meadow-way, closer, closer, until he caught the scent of the rabbit, nearer in the gloom, growling sullenly.

I spoke softly to him, and he, recognizing a fellow wanderer, spoke no more but turned away from the scent of the dead animal and from me into the night.

And he went his way and I mine.

B RAD had a dog once, a lovely thing, all soft fur and liquid eyes—bright and shining like diamonds—that watched so intently.

It was a half-breed sheepdog, a first cross I think farmers called such a dog, a cross between a Scotch collie and a

66

Border, but I was never very sure of such terms. It was a dog: that was sufficient. And it had a tail, unlike old Wall-eye, the shepherd's dog, that had but a bobble no bigger than the pom-pom on a girl's hat.

It was early evening when Brad came over the four-acre to my tent. I saw him when he was half a mile away as he came through the gateway where the old elm log lay in Bridgeclose; but his companion puzzled me. He had tied his handkerchief around the dog's neck (it had no collar) and was half dragging it over the field towards me. I could hear him coaxing the animal.

'Come on, old girl! There's a good girl!' But still the dog hung back, and he paused to pat the soft fur.

'What in the world have you got there?' I yelled as he drew nearer. And at the sound of my voice the dog tried to bolt, but Brad held her firmly by her fur and the handkerchief.

'Come quick!' he answered. 'Look! A dog! A beauty!'

I went over the field to him, and the sheepdog struggled again to escape.

Soon we were making a fuss of her, patting her ribs, stroking her hair and rubbing her ears, and in a while she condescended to be led to the tent.

My brother had found her in the thick blackthorn scrub in the low meadows where the thin trickling stream enters the wide brook; in a thicket which we called Slangy.

He had gone to inspect a few snares which he had placed there in the early morning, for there were many rabbit runs in the shaded undergrowth, many criss-crossing trails in the black leaf mould of years, and he was adept at finding the newly used bolt-gaps.

'I heard a bit of a slobbering,' explained Brad in answer to my natural inquiry. 'And there she was, feeding at a half-grown coney which had got itself caught in the snare! At first

I thought it was a fox. She ran away but I teased her wi' a bit of meat and she came to me, and here she is.'

'But . . .' I remonstrated, fingering the soft ear of the sheep-dog, 'you can't keep her. She belongs to someone! She's not yours.'

He had apparently thought of that. There must be some way out, he said.

'But our parents,' I urged. 'They'll never agree!'

And I was right.

We took the animal home and Brad explained the position to my mother. He argued, he pleaded, but it was of no avail.

'You'll take her to the police,' Mother insisted. 'You'd look well with a dog here! And who would feed it? You'll lodge it with the police, and don't dare to bring it back!' And reluctantly, sullenly, my brother and I went down the weedy drive, the sheepdog trotting between us, a little bewildered by the events of the day.

Now the village policeman, old Peabody, was an excellent official who rarely sought trouble. When we presented our-selves at his door complete with dog, and explained our mission, his face fell.

'You shouldn't have encouraged it,' he reproved. 'It would ha' perhaps found its own way home.'

We denied the suggestion, true though it was.

The constable put out a hand towards the dog, but she cringed away nervously.

'What's the name on the collar?' he asked hopefully. 'That'll tell us something.' But we had to confess that she wore no such adornment, and he swore softly.

'She's a nice dog,' said Brad brightly. 'I like her!'

'You would!' retorted Peabody with acidity. 'Why, in heaven's name, did you have to bring her to me? Why didn't you let her go? Here, give her to me!' He held out a reluctant hand.

Before complying, Brad spoke again.

'What will you do with her?' he asked. 'If you put her in your shed she'll have the place down. Mrs Peabody won't like that!'

The constable glared.

'Why didn't you think of that before, you blithering young idiot? I've got to put it up now that you've brought it. I don't want the thing. I know all about the howling!'

Brad spoke earnestly to him. We had, he explained, only done the correct thing in bringing lost property to the police. That was the law. Peabody looked very suspicious at Brad's sudden interest in the rights and wrongs of things. If, my brother continued, it was an inconvenience for the policeman to house the dog until its owner was found, would he not allow us to look after the animal?

A lurid picture was painted for Peabody's benefit of sleepless nights and howling dogs, and an angry wife, the whole canvas decorated with so many colourful verbal traceries that, at last, the policeman agreed to Brad's suggestion.

'But mind,' he warned. 'No foolery!'

And my brother promised, finger wet, finger dry.

I protested vehemently when we were out of hearing of Peabody.

'How on earth can you keep it?' I asked. 'They'll never let you have it at home! Mother'll be plain wild when she knows.'

'She ain't going to know,' answered Brad. 'Nobody'll know. That dog's mine! She's mine unless somebody claims her. She's mine!'

The dog wagged her tail as he talked and patted her head.

'But . . .' I began again.

'Look!' said Brad. 'It's almost dark now. Nobody will see you if you're careful.'

I gaped. I knew my brother and guessed what was in his mind.

'No!' I answered the unasked request. 'I'll not keep her at the tent. No fear! Not on your life!'

But Brad's powers of persuasion were great and the sheep-dog's were greater, for those soft moist eyes glowed at me even in the near dark.

She came with me as though she were going home. Once only she paused, and that was when Brad gave her a final pat and left us; then she stood still for a moment listening to his heavy boots ringing over the pebbled road.

She slept at my feet throughout the night. Once or twice she wakened me with a soft whimpering, but when I scolded her she quietened again and stretched her warm body against my bed, snuggling there until daybreak.

There is little sleep in the meadows after birdsong. The robin rouses the world and, after that, all the birds conspire to keep it awake. The blackbird chortles jocularly; no alarm now such as there was at night before he went to his roost. There is no fear so early in the morning; that comes only as the day ages.

Willow-warblers call in a fine chorus from the waterside where the sedge-chat joins with his hurried song; indeed all things sing, glad that the night is past.

As I opened the tent flap the sheepdog crept out, hesitantly, into the meadow and paused inquisitively to stare at me, but at my word she bounded forward into the damp grass and danced crazily over the ridge and furrow of the field, twisting and turning in a mad ecstasy as though released from prison and glad of the freedom. And after her joy had had its first fling she came to my side again almost apologetically, and looked expectantly up at my face as though waiting for further orders, but I had none to give her.

A cluster of sheep in an adjoining field gathered in a tight group on a small mound of earth and looked through the gappy hedge at my companion, and bleated miserably through the morning birdsong; and the bitch would have rounded them up and brought them to me if I had but given the command. She went forward a few yards in pretence, still without taking her moist brown eyes from my face, then back again to my side, once, twice, as though begging to be allowed to go about her usual work, but I turned from the sheep and went inside the tent, and she followed, puzzled and slightly aggrieved.

She shared my food at midday. I had made a stew over the stick fire; a hot-pot of odds and ends of vegetables and meat, and even as I was preparing the meal the animal became a little frantic for food, and a little dribble of saliva hung from her chops as I cut up the rabbit meat.

When the meal had been cooked she barked excitedly, and squatted before me as I ate. Each piece that I threw to her was caught in mid air and devoured ravenously, and as soon as one morsel had been consumed she barked for more. When the meal was over her appetite was still unappeased, and she foraged about among the pots by the tripod fireplace, hoping to find some scraps there, but there were none.

The warm afternoon was lazed away by both of us, and at early evening Brad came whistling over the meadow. The bitch heard him and barked lustily, but when she caught his scent she went towards him, rather nervously, and came with him to the tent.

'Did you bring any food for her?' I asked. 'Any bones or anything?'

Brad made a gesture of self-irritation with his hand and admitted that such a thing had not entered his head.

'We'll find her summat,' he said after a while. 'A rabbit or

a rat or something! Come on, lass!' he urged to the dog as he
rose to his feet.

He beckoned to me, and we went along the hedgerow of the
four-acre towards a rough bit of ground covered with a rank
growth of nettles and scrub which stood in a corner of the field
beyond, and there he tried to coax the sheepdog to enter the
roughage and hunt, but she cringed back, suspicious of his
intentions.

'Let her alone!' I suggested. 'She'll perhaps go in if we
keep out of the way,' and indeed that is what happened.

But all her searching led to nothing; there was neither rabbit
nor rat in the thicket, and soon the bitch tired of the fruitless
search.

We took her over many fields in that warm evening, by the
side of many hedges, but could find no food for her; and,
disconsolately, we wandered back to the tent.

'Haven't never known so few conies about!' grumbled
Brad as we walked along. I made some inadequate reply and
turned to sympathize with the dog, but she was not at our heels.

She had crouched on her belly fifty yards or so behind and
seemed most reluctant to follow us farther. All our whistling
and coaxing had no effect upon her, and when Brad went
towards her she rose sulkily and turned from him, slinking
away as though she feared a whipping.

'Good dog!' cajoled Brad. 'Good little girl! Come on,
then!' but it was no use.

Almost apologetically she left him, slinking away to the
secrecy of the hedge-stoles where she disappeared from our
view.

And that was the last we saw of her; yet we knew that she
had gone far down the valley and beyond the big smooth hill,
for the blackbirds yelled from the hedges as she passed by, and
the sheep gathered into small compact groups on isolated field

hillocks; farther and farther away, beyond Bogclose and Bankyclose, even to Hallows and Bratmyr where the sound of the chivvying blackbirds ceased.

For a long time we looked over to the westward, then turned abruptly away.

'She's gone!' cried Brad incredulously. 'She's gone!'

I nodded. I remembered the evening when Mary had gone too in the fading glow of the west.

'She'd nice eyes!' murmured Brad, still thinking of the dog.

'Yes!' I agreed absently, for my thoughts were elsewhere.

As SOON as the corn is cut and gathered, cub-hunting begins in the country. Then all the young are taught their lessons—some necessary, some not.

There is no set time of the year as in fox-hunting proper, which opens with much pomp and ceremony in the early days of November. Cub-hunting just happens, without fuss or bother, at a time when most of the world is waking from sleep; a haphazard affair; the corn carried and the training commences for the young hounds and the fox cubs, the ponies and the chubby-faced children who should still be abed; all preparing for the later intensity of the chase.

Brad told me of the meet.

'Half past six,' he said on the previous night. 'At the lake-side. They're rousting that set of cubs that were born in the bank-holes.'

74

I did not ask how he knew. That was accepted.

'It'll be good sport! I'll call round for you about six.'

It is not very reasonable—for fox-hunting was always taken more or less for granted in the district—but I got a big thrill from watching the meet; the sight of the keen hounds and the song of the huntsman's horn; the view of the fox as he struck over the green fields; the startled sheep betraying his run and, above all, the crisp morning.

I envied the mounted folk when the November meets were held close to the village, for, on foot as we were, there was much chasing but little chance of keeping with the hunt when a strong line took them over the territory. In the more gentle pace of cub-disturbing one could always be up with the hounds and riders; one felt on more equal terms with the rest of the learners.

The morning brought a few gems of dew to the hedgerow spider-webs and to the spread gossamer of the grass, and this was not unusual nor unexpected, for I had come to look for pearls at break of day, and was rarely disappointed.

There was wine in the air too before the stuffiness of day arrived; a nectar that made the blood race in my veins as I ran over the grass to the cattle-drink, there to wash.

And not in mine alone. Birdsong came in a flood with the sun; an after-moult song, almost as intense as the matins of early spring; a surprising chorus of blackbirds and thrushes, wrens and willow-wrens, sedge-chats and finches; all joining in with the bleating lambs and the planning swallows. All the month-lost song was back again at last after so long a wait.

It is the morning song of birds that awakens the heart of the world. August is such a sterile month, a time of drowse and no trying, for there is no bird music to set the world to a pace; but after the rest the music all comes back again, and none the worse.

F

No blackbirds warned as Brad came over the fields towards the tent—for birds are tame in the early morning; the day has not yet brought fear—and, when he peeped into the dark of the tent with inquiry in his eyes, I pulled on my rough woollen jersey and indicated that I was ready to accompany him; and even as we went upwards to the hill beyond where the lake lay, we heard the 'clip-clop' of the horses on the hard road.

'They're on time,' muttered Brad. 'They'll be going down the mere road. We'll cut across the stubble. We'll be there before the hounds,' and we fell into a jog-trot over the rough fields on our way to the lake spinneys.

There seems always a strange unreality about cubbing, which the more advanced sport of fox-hunting does not possess. Perhaps it is because of the ungodly hour at which it begins, for six o'clock of a morning is a fantastic time for so much desperate activity in the quiet country.

Softly the neat and tidy people came to the blackthorn copse where the meet was to be held, all sleep gone from their eyes. Horses and hounds appeared as if by magic over the hillside that led from Holloway, the cool, smiling huntsman talking to his pack as he brought them down the sloping meadow to the waterside.

He spoke in high-pitched hound talk, a shrill falsetto, 'Ee-we! Ee-we! Eee my beauties! Pr-r-r-r! Pr-r-r-r! Ee! Lee, lee!' and the lumbering hounds looked up at him expectantly, whimpering a little and yelping when—having strayed from the pack—the whip's snaking lash caught them on the buttocks.

'Wanderer, Wanderer, there!'

Little time was wasted at the spinney side, a few pleasantries with some of the older foot-followers; a doffing of the hat to one of the more important ladies who had come to see how her young hopeful behaved; and, after consulting with the Master, the cool huntsman gave certain instructions to his whips and they disappeared to take up their stations at inconspicuous places around the blackthorn bushes.

Other horsemen followed, trotting their mounts to favourite positions as though by habit. Little six-year-old children on shaggy ponies moved with the rest, but their grooms kept a careful eye on them less they should stray too far.

White gulls circled the water—out of place so far from the sea—laughing at the early disturbance, but the swans were too disdainful to take wing, and rode away from the sags and the reedmace trash at the water inlet, and drifted majestically with their dun-coloured young away from the noise, raising their wings and arching their necks from time to time in protest.

Away on the opposite side of the lake, in a field of green aftermath, sat a girl on a grey horse, a solitary figure, statuesque, on guard, listening to the song of the hounds as they crashed through the undergrowth, and the incessant threshing of the huntsman's stock on his saddle.

On adjacent hilltops too sat others on calm mounts, watching for the bolting fox, ready to mark his escape route, to mark his line like veterans, these young women of the break of day, bright-eyed tranquil morning goddesses, seventeen summers old.

Brad and I stood a little away from the rest of the field, on a slight incline which gave us a good view of the bushes where they sloped down to the lake.

There was a wide patch of buff sedge on the strand of mud between the spinney and the water on to which one or two of the hounds drifted from time to time until chided back again by the voice of the huntsman.

'Not much music,' grumbled Brad. 'Nowt in there by the sound of it.'

We could hear the thin voice of the man in scarlet echoing on the clear air of the morning, urging the pack, and soon he emerged from the blackthorn scrub into the open of the waterside.

He raised his horn to his lips and there was a flurry of a tune and the whole of the pack spewed out on to the sedges, scenting low to the ground, unsighted in the thickness of the vegetation, but told by their waving brushes.

Old Warden, the big dog-hound, bayed loudly, and a dozen tails went hurriedly towards the sound, crying excitedly as they too picked up the scent of the inlying fox.

One or two of the hounds burst through the cover of the sags and came to view by the waterside, and others, in their anxiety, splashed noisily through the shallow water, stirring up the black mud in a mad desire to reach a scent, and soon the quiet lake was alive with noise.

The red-coat dismounted—handing the reins to a gaping hanger-on—and went into the mud and sedge-blades after his pack, slapping his riding boots with his stock, cracking expertly the long lash of his whip and encouraging the hounds with his purring voice.

'Li-ew! Li-ew! Up, m'girl! Le-ep! Pr-r-r-r! Pr-r-r-r!'

They sang joyously, and mixed with their music was the yelp of the terrier, an excited, imitative noise, thin and inadequate when compared with his betters.

'They're on him now!' Brad whispered. 'Watch the hedgerows! If it's an old 'un he'll skulk away. The cubs'll take a bit more shifting!'

Young children—scarcely old enough to walk, one would think—sat more upright on their tiny tubby ponies and smiled happily at one another over a few yards of ground; and all so early on this fine morning; seven o'clock and the cattle in the valley going to their milking, and fooling about with the cowman's dog; and young things afraid by the waterside, afraid of sudden death on this fine morning.

Little children sat happily waiting.

There was an abrupt silence, broken only by the purring 'Pr-r-r-r' of the huntsman, and soon this drifted away as he took his pack over the dying sedges towards the farther end of the lake.

Knowledgeable foot-folk moved slowly to the water-head, anticipating that the hounds would break cover on the opposite bank, but as they went forward one of the more observant set up a screaming shriek.

'Ya, ya, ya! Tallyo back!' A strong tawny fox glided through the hedgerow, through a gap between the now yelling people who kicked out wildly at the fugitive as he passed.

More yells came from the ploughland, indicating the escape path of the fox, and a smiling whip came along in answer to the calls.

So many excited folk tried to point out the direction which the fleeing animal had taken, and he listened politely for a moment or two but took note only of a little old man who stood close in to the hedgerow.

'Ould dog-fox, Fred. Gone up'ards to Short's goss, along the ould line.'

The slim whip nodded almost curtly to the old man, smiled charmingly and thanked the rest of the foot-folk and galloped back again to the hound music which had begun again in the sags at the far end of the lake and beyond, where a thin spinney lay in the valley, obscured from our view.

A shot rang out from over the hill whence the tip-tailed fox had gone, and a flock of squawking daws and rooks rose above Holloway like a puff of smuts, and for some time they circled over the spinneys, but there was no more firing and they flew back to the tree tops.

Faintly now came the noise of the hounds, and the huntsman's whip-cracks were no longer audible.

Old Jake, the waterkeeper, trudged slowly across the sags and mud-trash which had been trodden almost flat by the hounds, and at times he paused and looked around at the mess, as though reviewing the morning's work.

I turned to speak to Brad, but he had gone.

There were few foot-folk about now; most of them were still chasing after the pack, and I thought that perhaps my brother had gone with them, but I had seen enough to enjoy and did not follow.

A big hound came from the blackthorn scrub, a laggard, licking his chops, having found something to his liking in the bushes, but he was the last of the hounds at the lakeside. All the unimportant clatter had ended.

A robin sang a little song and the willows rustled, and water-birds settled again. Only from the deep distance came the sound of hooves on the metalled road.

The yellow muck-flies swarmed on the strange new drop-pings left by the tubby ponies after the disturbing hullabaloo, and skimming swallows danced above the meadows again.

Now the sun was high above the hills, and the morning well born.

And when all had gone, a few patient fishermen strode slowly over the water fringe and sat in the stink of the churned-up mud.

All the gross noises passed in the clop of horses' hooves and, at last, the day settled down to its peace.

I walked gently back over the fields, from stile to hedge-gap, in a straight way, for it was much farther by the hard road and not so kind to the feet.

Two women gleaners were still at work in the stubble as I passed through the cut field, yet there could have been little there for them, for the corn had been carried long before and many village folk had earlier collected most of the wheat heads.

One of the women straightened her back and spoke as I approached.

'Where they gone, boyo?'

I pointed to the valley and told her in which direction the hounds were running, at which she grunted and went on with her picking.

The sheep were beginning to settle again after the disturbance of the meet, but they ran into little groups again as I passed by whistling on this fine morning, and a farm hand, two fields away, yelled a greeting and waved, and his collie came over the intervening distance to be petted, scampering back again to its master after I had rubbed its head.

'Hallo, boyo!' I held up my hand in acknowledgment and went my way.

I sensed that there was someone at my tent long before I reached the stile that led into the four-acre. And I did not rely on intuition alone.

There are many signs in the open country that tend to indicate the presence of a human being. A pigeon, winging through the sky, will suddenly veer away from a stack of hay where a cowman is cutting a wedge of feeding for his herd.

A wren will creel again and again when it sees a squatting figure of the rabbit-catcher skulking; and gulls will circle a blackthorn spinney by the waterside just so long as the gunman remains hidden there.

Blackbirds yell at prowling people, but then they are full of alarm at all times and do not always speak the truth.

But the jay never lies, and the rest of the world trusts to his word.

As I approached the four-acre, I saw chaffinches and yellow-hammers fidgeting on the hedge twigs in the corner where stood my tent, and a robin—which had its nest in a rusty tin kettle in the thick hawthorn branches—'tucked' in annoyance,

Then I was sure that something was amiss, for they took little notice of me when I was at home. They had become used to me and, in a lesser degree, to Brad too. Today they were pothering in quite a different manner, rather as they had done when we took the stray dog to the tent.

Quietly as I approached, I had already been seen by the intruder, and a voice rang out across the field.

'Hey! Boyo! Come here quickly!'

I leaped the stile and there, by the tent, saw my brother bending over some strange object.

'What on earth . . .!' I began

'It's all right,' he reassured. 'You come and help me!'

Stretched on four upright lengths of stick was the pelt of a fox, a fine skin, at which Brad was scrubbing with a handful of grass, whilst in a half-circle around him lay other bloody grass wads, discarded after their service.

Then I realized why the birds had been uneasy.

A horrible stink of dead fox pervaded the whole atmosphere and I retched a little, but Brad took no notice.

'Where did you get that thing?' I demanded. 'What are you going to do with it? Where's the rest of it?'

'You help clean it up!' he replied. 'I'll tell you all about it later. You clean round its brush!'

He scraped away at the head of the pelt, working like a demon until all the blood marks had gone. Satisfied, he lifted the pelt from the four sticks and carried it a few yards into the field. There he stretched it over a framework of more sticks and left it to dry in the sun, and for a while the blue flies had a feast.

'Where did you get it?' I asked again. 'It's fresh killed! Where did you find it?'

'I'll get something for that,' he said, ignoring my question. 'I'll get plenty for that skin. You wait! A shilling or even more! They make grand furs!'

Then, after much more talk, he told me how he had obtained the dead animal.

'I left you at the waterside,' he reminded me. 'Well, that was after I heard that shot. That racket came from old Shenton's farm, and that was the way the fox went when he broke cover, eh?'

He looked at me for my agreement. I nodded.

'And then?' I asked.

'Well, you see! I knew Shenton wouldn't have a fox on his land if he could help it, so I went over the hill to see what had happened after I heard the shooting, and there, by the side of a dead ash tree, I found this, still warm and wi' a hole in its side. I shoved it up my jersey and came here over the old mere road.'

'Didn't Shenton see you?' I asked. 'Surely he must have done!'

'Oh yes!' answered my brother. 'He saw me all right! Threatened to shoot me too, but we talked a bit and came to an understanding.' He said this almost grandly. 'And we agreed to say nothing about it. I'm satisfied. So's he, I think! He doesn't like the hunt!'

I knew that, and the reason for his quarrel.

During the latter part of the previous season—the time when the early lambs were in the fields—he had lost one or two in-lamb ewes and had several more badly mauled by the pack as they chased an outlier fox over the farmer's land.

The fox—an old rogue dog—had been forced from a patch of rough ground by the side of the valley brook, and in his initial dash for safety had left the field far behind.

There was much wire about at the time, and the huntsman—forced to the gateways when the more direct path over the hedges was barred to him—lost touch temporarily with his pack, and the crafty fox, heading the hounds by the length of a field, ran upwards with a flock of startled sheep, ran close with them so that his rank scent tainted their long wool. When the leading hound came up to the sheep he was confused by the wealth of scent and hungry for blood, and he bit where the fox scent lay. Others joined in and soon that corner of the meadow was not good to look upon.

When the huntsman arrived on the scene, cursing roundly all farmers who wired their fences, he took in the situation at once and, drawing a pistol from his deep pocket, dispatched the leader of the pack on the spot.

The rest of the hounds answered their master's call at once and were reprieved, but the leader that had fallen so far from grace suffered the extreme penalty.

'Pity!' murmured the huntsman to his whip. 'But we could never have trusted him again. Get him buried!' and the water-keeper dug a deep hole by the side of the ditch.

The circumstances were explained later to Farmer Shenton who, not unnaturally, took it badly. He was duly compensated for the loss, but from that day the hounds were not welcomed over his land.

'I'll deal wi' the foxes in my own way,' he said.

I LOOKED at the skin stretched out on the wooden frame.

'But you can't do anything with it!' I argued. 'It'll need dressing properly, not just saltpetre and alum.' That was our own crude recipe for preserving moleskins and such like. 'It'll have to be properly done.'

'That's all right,' replied Brad. 'Whoever I sell it to will have that done. You see! I'll get a bob or more for it!' and he smiled happily at the thought. 'I'm off now. Let it stay there till I come again. I'll be back again when I've sold it.' He held up a finger. 'This evening I'll come for it. You see!'

He went over the meadow, whistling shrilly, leaving me to clear up the mess of discarded grass tufts which lay about the camp.

There was a faint tang on the air caused by the curing skin, and because of this I strolled over the fields to the little brook, away from the tent site.

There and thereabouts I stayed through the clean afternoon, drinking at the ooze of spring water that welled up between a small heap of white pebbles; calling to the birds; bringing down the high-flying bullfinch to a perch on the bush where I sat in the shade; imitating the melancholy 'pee-it' of the willow-warbler until he, tiring of the game, climbed to a higher branch and, as though in challenge, sang a tripping stanza, far beyond my power of accomplishment.

A dumpy red vole came to look at me, and I kept quiet whilst it was almost at my feet, but from the sky drifted a hunting kestrel, hovering menacingly over the meadow in search of food. Turning to watch the falcon, I swung my foot, and the vole scampered away into the grass tussocks, unaware of the greater danger.

When the daisy heads began to close and show the pink of their undersides, I heard Brad's whistle from over the Wrang-lands and hurried back to my tent.

He told me that he had sold the skin for fifteen pence.

'Fred Fallows has bought it,' he said. 'He's getting married and going to live in old Beth's cottage. Having the pelt made up for his gel to get married in.' He hesitated a moment, then said thoughtfully:

'Fancy anyone wearing one of those things round their neck! Stinking things for fine ladies!'

Fifteen pence for half a dozen lives; the fox, the handsome, scent-bewitched hound, a pair of blarting sheep and a few unborn lambs; that's cheap enough!

Brad took the skin away with him and I was glad to see the back of it. Dead things lying about the tent site made the place untidy.

Beth was very old, a little mite of a woman, wizened and creased as a long-kept apple.

She had lived in the village all her life and had never travelled farther than one or other of the adjoining hamlets. The older folks said that in her youth Beth had been a lovely slip of a girl.

'A fine little wench!' as one old dodderer put it.

Now there was little to show of her beauty.

She was quite mad. Not raving nor violent, but silly-mad, childish they said, as though madness were a trait of the very young.

I saw her often in the fields and by the clay banks of the canal, gathering clover-knobs and the broad leaves of the

foalsfoot which she used as tobacco, smoking the evil con-
coction in a little stumpy black clay pipe.

Sometimes she would wander across to my tent and mouth
at me and try to talk in a thin, high-pitched voice, but I could
not understand what she said.

Like a child she would touch my arm and shamble away for
a few steps, inviting me to some sort of a tig game, and when I
made no attempt to chase her—as the children of the village
used to—then she would lament and the tears stream down
her face in disappointment.

I would give her a little of my food and send her off happily
over the fields, clutching at the morsel as though it were
precious.

She joined in the children's games with the rest of them,
although much against their will, for she stole their marbles
and screamed in anger when they tried to recover them. Then
they were accused of ill-treating the old crone.

Strangely enough the children accepted Beth as one of
them, slapping her when she tried to join them in their mass
skipping game, sitting her on the grass verge and deputing one
of their number to look after her, which they did by feeding
her with the wild blackberries and other hedge fruits or by
refilling her dirty clay pipe.

She played snobs with them on the swanky new paving
stones in front of the church, sitting awkwardly on the level
slabs, watching like a hawk lest one of her young companions
should make a mistake; taking her turn and expertly manipu-
lating the five pebbles as good as the best of them. That much
was left of her own childhood.

In the evening, when he had finished his work on the farm,
her only son—a giant of a fellow, dull-witted and morose—
came to the playing children and led his mother away from
them.

Sometimes she screamed and kicked like a mardy child, but he was very gentle with her, and when she became too intractable he would lift her in his strong arms, place the clay pipe in her mouth, and carry her home as a father would a struggling baby, soothing her all the time.

No one made much of it as they went through the long village street to their cottage; folks had become accustomed to such scenes.

When the ragged griddler came to the village she followed him as he sang his dirgeful songs, joining in at times in her squeaky, tuneless voice.

When he chased her away she spat at him and swore.

Old Ben, the gipsy chair-mender, tolerated her, however, as he sat on the square of grass in the centre of the village, repairing odds and ends of broken furniture.

His visits had begun to grow less frequent now, for he was ageing; almost as old as old Beth herself.

'I'm getting a bit beyond padding about in that thar stream looking for rushes, boyo! Too old! Too old! Mi' chessy giz me 'ell at times, boyo!' and as though to emphasize this fact he would cough harshly.

He grinned at Beth as she sat in front of him, and she grinned back, mouthing some strange pleasantries, to which Ben responded with a knowing 'Ar!' pretending to understand her, laughing with her yet not neglecting his work. But when she would have helped him with the rush chair-seats he pushed her away, and then she would sulk.

Beth was not entirely neglected of course. Her big son kept their little cottage reasonably clean and did most of the necessary chores, but there were certain things that he could not do.

The preparation of food was a problem, for the man was so long at his work; but a kindly neighbour saw to it that old Beth did not starve during his absence. She also cooked a meal for him each night when he came home, and performed many gratuitous tasks for the gloomy man and his mad mother, and all from the kindness of her heart.

But one day that heart gave a sudden lurch and she fell slowly on to the thick rug that covered the hearth.

When big Tom came home late that night there was no smell of hot meal to greet him, and he walked over to his neighbour's cottage to seek the reason.

There he found the kind lady lying on the thick hearthrug, his mother sitting beside her, playing with the ringlets of her white hair.

The lady was not dead; her heavy breathing told the man that much, but he knew that she was seriously ill, and he carried his screaming mother away, locked her in her own house and went for Peabody, the policeman.

The doctors shook their heads gravely when they saw the lady later.

'She'll want careful nursing,' they said. 'Someone must look after her.'

Peabody wrote off to the sick woman's relatives, and in due course a large black conveyance drew up at the door and two men carried her gently from the house.

She had recovered sufficiently to say a few words to Big Tom and to lay her hand in blessing on old Beth's head.

'I don't know how you'll go on with her now,' she whispered weakly to the big morose man. 'I'm so sorry for you.'
Tom shuffled uneasily and took her small frail hand in his.

'Don't you worry, ma'am! You've been good to us! Your folk'll be good to you.'

Her house was let to a couple too engrossed in their own affairs to bother about old Beth and her son, who were left to fend as best they could.

One day Tom failed to turn up at his work, and the farmer

sent the crow-boy to see what had happened, but the boy found only the old woman weeping over an empty grate.

Her son had gone and no one knew where. There were rumours of course. People said that he had 'gone for a soldier', but the truth of it was that Tom had broken under the strain of his home life and he had run from it.

Old Beth was taken to the poorhouse in the little market town, and there she soon pined for her child companions and passed away, weeping.

When it had happened and all was done with, many people in the village were sympathetic, kindly disposed; but that was after Beth and Tom had gone. Few folk really minded, not even the snob-playing children, for Beth had been a bit of a nuisance.

At the time I thought little of the occurrence; it concerned me not at all except to make me sad when I thought of those folk whom I had known so well, and that now were gone.

And in such a moment of sadness my heart suddenly thumped against my ribs, for I realized that the kind old lady was Mary's last remaining relative in the village, and now that she had gone the link with her was broken.

I knew in that moment that I should perhaps never see Mary again.

Brad came to my tent and I sent him away.

'What's up?' he asked. 'Your eyes are all red. Are you all right?'

I nodded.

'It's about time you broke your tent, y' know,' he advised coaxingly. 'You come home, boyo!'

Again I shook my head.

'You go now!' I pleaded. 'I'm all right, really. I just want to sit quiet.'

Solicitously he built up my fire—although the evening was

G

quite warm—and went back again over to the Ramshorn gate, pausing there to look back at me.

After he had gone I sought comfort, not at the fireside, but down by the waterside, looking to where Mary and I had spent our few hours together, dwelling on those memories, getting nothing but heartache and satisfied with that.

Yet I wanted to take the whole picture of the canalway and the bushes, the wild flowers and the weeds, as they were then, so that, I told myself tragically, I would ever remember them.

I could perhaps have chosen a better time, a season when the may was a-flower, when the roses hung on the hedges, or the sentimental forget-me-nots were peeping through the sedges, pleading to be gathered; but today there was little that was not past its best.

The sun was not much higher than the tops of the hedgerow elm trees, and a man's shadow lay almost ten yards along the ground.

The countryside was quiet except for the faint noise of children playing in the village street beyond Ramshorn and Wranglands; that and the soft whistle of the wood-pigeon's pinions as he left the elder bush and flew to the four-acre.

A few heads of white clover still flowered on the sloping bank; some round and plump, shapely and fragrant, not yet visited by the bees; others draped with a skirt of browning florets, fertilized past their best.

The shadows grew still longer on the grass. Those of the hedge elm reached across to the other side of the canal, and soon they disappeared altogether for a while when the sun hid behind the narrow horizon clouds, only to return—more lank than ever—when it peeped through a chink between the low cloud and the edge of Tythorn.

A little light fell on the seeded thistle-heads in the hedgerow where the scytheman's tool had not reached, but the evening sun could give to them none of its own colour, only a dinginess, an unwashed white, the hue of old sheeps' wool caught up on the fencing wire.

Somewhere farther down the canal side a water-hen croaked in alarm and another answered, and the quiet evening echoed to the calls which awakened the rest of the nodding birds.

The thrushes creaked as I passed by and the partridges talked in their petulance from the meadows, but the rooks only muttered as they flew overhead to the vicarage trees, grumbling to themselves like old men.

I looked over to the bushes where we had sat the length of a summer day. So short a time ago, and yet the freshness had gone, and now there was a blaze of adult colour on the sloping bank.

Some of the bushes were a maze of flaming orange, others gold. One shrub was the gold of ripe corn, another—its near companion—the colour of clover honey. There were fingers of chrome on the leaning ash, and a darker fume of its reflection in the still water.

All the bushes were reflected there, and the dying sedges too; each contorted slightly by the ripples made by the fidgeting water-hens which, hidden, were well aware of my presence.

A clumsy slip, however, and one of the more nervous birds flew, legs a-trail, from under the near bank to the other side of the canal; and now the coloured reflections fairly danced in the disturbed water before settling again.

Almost silently a water-vole entered the water, scarcely rippling the surface, but causing a narrow writhing band of mud to appear on the canal bed as he discreetly left for his hide lower down the stream.

In the fading twilight the mardy blackbirds gave no peace with their incessant alarms; and soon I forgot a little of my own sudden heartache and teased the birds, imitating them, and for some time we had a laughing quarrel by the waterside.

The colour went from the bushes and the reflections grew dark and forbidding, forming a sullen background for the lighter lily leaves.

Only the dead pallid stalks of the cow parsnip cast any light on the water now; those, and the aftermath of day which lay in a long pale ribbon, the length of the canal.

The creatures of the night came out, some tentatively, some furtively, as though afraid of the half-glare of twilight—the voles and the pipistrelles; the stoats and the soft-winged owls; all impatient for their time.

A little calmer now, and less unhappy, I went to my tent, for there was no more of day; the moon had taken over and it was night.

BRAD stopped suddenly, waved me to a halt then darted to the cover of the hedgerow.

'What's up?' I asked as we crouched in the dead nettles. He pointed to a bank in a corner of the field, and there I saw the figure of a man leaning on a green lichened stile.

We watched him in silence.

The afternoon was cold, for it was towards the close of the year and there had been neither rain nor sun for a week or more, and now each day there was a mist on the meadows and among the spindly pines in the fox covert. The grass was still green on the pasture, but a dull matt green as though the colour had been petrified on the blades by the cold mist; unpolished by the sun; a sameness, devoid of shades and light tints except where a diamond of dew winked from the cocks-foot grass or from the gossamer webs that covered the nettle beds like a veil.

We had been in the fields all the afternoon 'just looking round', as my brother put it, and now we were on our way home.

It was a month or more since I had struck my tent in the four-acre, reluctantly, but at the express command of my parents, and I was beginning to settle down—more or less—to life within four walls, hoping all the while for spring, lazing and disgruntled.

During the afternoon we had laid snares for rabbits, but had been unsuccessful. There was but one outlier in the fields, and, when we tried to drive it to the gappy hedge where Brad had set the wires, it doubled back again and vanished along the deep brown ridges of the newly turned plough furrows.

We had disturbed a fox on his way to the kale bed and had chased him over that same field of spliced earth, ya-hoo-ing wildly as though we were urging in a pack of hounds, but the sleek one soon outpaced us on the uneven ground, and we halted, breathless and laughing, at the rickety half-gate that led to the bridle-way.

Brad had mentally noted the linnet flocks and the charm of goldies on the thistles, and had grunted happily.

'We'll come for a few of them,' he said. Most of his pocket-money came from selling these captives.

'The nets! It'll be the nets!' he said. 'In a few days.' Ruminating: 'Daren't leave it too long or they'll be gone!'

We moved to the rise in the ground where, many years ago,

stood the old mill. On the forward slope of the field a thin
ash-pole spinney obscured our view of the valley, and it was
from that direction that Brad was looking so intently.

'Come under cover!' he said softly. 'There's something
going on down there beyond the spinney.'

I listened, hand to ear.

'Can hear a dog yapping,' I answered. 'That's all.'

'There's more than one,' replied Brad. 'There's a dozen
or more.'

'What is it?' I asked impatiently. 'Come on, let's go home.
There's nothing here for us!'

But Brad took no notice of my peevishness. He beckoned
to me and we moved forward; and now I could hear the commotion in the valley. It seemed as though a pack of yelping
dogs had been turned loose.

We looked at each other and grinned.

'It's the whippets!' I cried. 'This will be good sport.'

The whippets racing on Thorney. Brad nodded. Downhill
we raced towards the sound, running like mad things to the
spinney beyond which we knew were the dogs, but when we
would have climbed the fence into the Thorney field a gruff
voice spoke to us. It was the man at the stile.

'Eh! You! Where're you off?'

We gaped. Brad stuttered a little as he replied.

'We're . . . you see . . . could we go in?'

'Yes, if you pay. Iv'rybody's got to pay! Twopence
apiece!' he demanded.

Twopence! That was almost a fortune to us at that moment,
for we had hardly begun our bird-catching season, and what
little money we had acquired had been expended on lime and
snare wire and suchlike things, all costly requisites which had
to be replaced at the beginning of our season.

We had taken many rabbits, certainly, but they had been

used in the home and none to spare for outside customers; and for these home-consumed articles we received nothing—naturally. Neither did we question the rights and wrongs of this, although Brad would sometimes say wryly: 'Freeman's' after we had caught a particularly fine coney from the hedgerow and which we knew to be destined for the stock-pot or the stew-jar.

Twopence apiece! We hadn't a farthing.

Brad coaxed and pleaded like an evangelist, but the man in corduroys was adamant.

'Twopence apiece!' he repeated stolidly, and, when Brad added threats to his pleas, the big fence-keeper leaped the obstacle with the surprising agility of a cat and boxed our ears, and as we turned to fly from him we each received an adroitly placed kick on the buttocks that speeded our departure.

'You come again, that's all!' he called after us, but we had no intention of accepting his invitation.

'What do we do now?' I asked Brad when we had run far enough to be out of danger.

The whippets were yelping excitedly again, but we could not see them, for over the hedge the ground rose to a hillocky ridge, and the racing was beyond that point.

We attempted to force a way through the hedge-stoles and were partly successful, but old Corduroy Pants had anticipated the move and, as soon as our heads appeared through the trash of the hedgeside, he yelled again and came hell-for-leather down the ditchway, a long elder wand in his hand.

Hastily we withdrew and moved reluctantly away from the field, muttering under our breath dire threats against all who wore stinking corduroys.

Suddenly from beyond the hill there was a wild commotion. The whines of the whippets changed to a high-pitched excited scream, and men began to shout like maniacs.

'Ye-he! Liew, liew!' They urged the dogs on. Louder grew
the noise; excited voices; excited dogs, all joined together in a
long crescendo until it reached its peak in the thin squeal of a
dying rabbit, the game for the racing dogs; then the voices
dropped again to a low murmur, broken only by a disgruntled
backer disputing his winnings, and the miserable whimperings
of the rest of the whippets awaiting their turn to run.

Both Brad and I were a little excited by the music of the
racing, and we ran wildly away from the spinney and from the
guardian of the fence, desperately round to the other side of
the field to where a large white gate gave official entrance to
the pitch.

A few latecomers were passing through the opening, paying
their entrance monies to the attendants.

'There's old Bill Larker at the gate,' whispered Brad.

'We'll get nothing from him! Old Brunt's there too!' I
answered. 'He's a miserable devil! He won't let us in, you see!'
And I was right. We asked to be allowed inside the gate.

'Only just by the hedge, Mr Larker. We won't go right
in.' But we had our ears boxed and were driven off.

'No place for kids!' said Brunt gruffly, and disconsolately
we walked away.

We wandered round the edge of the field, inspecting each
gap, each thin part of the hawthorn, but those places were well
guarded by one or other of the local officials who had organized
the affair, and soon we began to despair of getting a viewpoint.
But then we had a stroke of luck.

As the preliminary arrangements were being made for the
next race, Brad noticed that the person whose job it was to
patrol a rather gappy stretch of hedge became over-interested
in the proceedings, remaining in the one spot by the fence, his
eyes glued to the competing whippets.

'Come on!' whispered Brad. 'Keep close to me down the

hedge. Make for that thin bit against the rotten elm! We'll see it all from the ditch. He'll not see us once we get there!'

Stealthily we went now, crouching by the nettle-clad bankside until we reached the padded ditch over which arched a roof of year-old thorns.

By sheer good luck we had found a hide which was excellent for our purpose. The wide butt of the elm shielded us from the guard whilst he remained at his post by the fence, and we knew that the thorns would hide us when he should come a-seeking for such folk as us who wanted the sport free of payment.

Once comfortably in the ditch we raised our heads and looked over the meadow, and Brad breathed a joyous 'Oh-h-h', for there, stretched out before us, was the whole panoply of the whippets' racing field; the dogs, the handlers, the groups of betting men, the coloured arm-bands of the spotter—that most professional of men upon which so much depended in the game.

A quiet fell on the people gathered behind the officials at the other end of the field, an anticipatory silence broken at times by the sharp cry of one of the betting men.

'Gi' yer evens agin Sal! Goo on! Evens!' and a knot of mufflered men formed around the owner of the voice, some to accept his odds, some to watch their fellows part with their money.

The lean athletic spotter went behind the crowd to where a small wizened man stood in charge of a large sack, and into this he plunged a long arm. There was a frantic surging inside the bag and, after a moment, the spotter brought forth a struggling rabbit from the rest of its wretched companions confined there in the darkness.

These were the quarries of the racing dogs. Earlier in the day they had been taken from the burrows in the disused sandpit; captured at break of day, before the sun was an hour old; a dozen or more forced from their hides by the writhing ferret;

relentlessly pursued underground until, in desperation, they left the doubtful security of the warren and made for the escape hole in the thorn ditch.

In their terror they had not seen the purse-net which guarded the exit, and, as they plunged wildly forward to the circle of daylight, the string of the net tightened and the soft trap closed around them.

Every bolt-hole held a net, and every net a rabbit, until a dozen or more were collected and placed, terrified and panting, in the large sack.

There they lay throughout the rest of the morning, squatting almost motionless in the dark, motionless too when, in the early morning—hours after their capture—they were rudely lifted and thrown over the little wizened man's shoulder and carried to the field where the races were now being held.

A whippet whined as the animal in the spotter's hands struggled, but there was no escape. The lean man held it firmly by the ears and the slack skin of its back, and carried it to the dogs, showing it not only to the dogs paired and ready for the next race, but to the rest of the trembling, excited creatures that stood leashed, awaiting their turn: teasing them with the squirming rabbit; urging them into a yelping fury with the promise of the prize; withdrawing it an inch away from their wet muzzles.

The two dogs that were next to race were driven almost mad with the tormenting, and when they could not reach the bait they set upon each other, worrying and snarling, until their handlers separated them.

And as the spotter went to his releasing mark twenty yards or so away from the dogs, the same handlers argued, quarrelled, and themselves fell to a one-armed fighting, holding securely on to their dogs nevertheless until called to order by the peremptory tone of the starter.

'Come on! Come on, now!'

There was a sudden feeling of tension as the spotter reached his post. The whining of the dogs became louder and louder until there was an unearthly din over the meadows, but the men were quiet, attentive. Even the betting men were silent as the handlers crouched over their charges. Now they gripped the dogs by the collar and rump, ready for the start.

From our peep-hole in the thorn ditch we saw the starter raise his hand. The lanky spotter bent to the ground and suddenly hurled the rabbit from him, and at that moment the starter dropped his hand and the handlers of the two whippets threw the trembling dogs forward, each striving to give his own favourite the advantage of a good start.

The whippets sped like the wind, seeming scarcely to touch the ground as they flew over the level turf on legs that seemed too slight to support even their fine-drawn bodies.

Such delicate things were the whining whippets, lovely in their misery when crouched and shivering, tail down and back a-hump when waiting in the lines; lovely in their speed and utter grace over the dull green of the winter meadows.

Straight towards us came the rabbit, mazed and confused by its sudden freedom, and the spotter ran after it for a while until the dogs came up to him and in sight of the racing animal. Then their speed became even greater, and any thoughts that Brad may have had of capturing the hunted one for himself was soon put out of his mind, for it became obvious that the whippets would be upon it before it reached the hedge.

They killed it twenty yards away from us, in a little dip in the ground. Floss, the buff and white bitch that wore the red ribbon at her neck, first rolled it over, and the rabbit screamed in fear. Before it could rise again Sal of the white ribbon was up to it too, and in a while the screams ceased and the bitches came away from the game and stood apart, a little undecided, until Sal went again to the body. Then the other bitch flew forward to the usurper and a snarling fight went on until their handlers came to separate them, and then they quarrelled between themselves as they had done before.

The spotter raised his right arm, the arm upon which was tied a red handkerchief, and the betting man paid out their money on the result.

Brad inclined his head towards me.

'What do you think of it?' he whispered.

I had not been impressed by the spectacle and told him so. What little I had seen was sufficient for me, and I was ready to go and leave both dogs and men to their quarrels and killing.

'Aye! It ain't much to look at!' agreed my brother. 'It's poor sport I should think.' He listened. 'Sh-h-h! Keep down!' We dropped low in the ditch. Faint footsteps were coming towards us.

'It's old Hawky! He's come to look round the gaps,' explained Brad. 'Keep down! He'll not see us!'

We heard Hawky muttering and mumbling as he passed by our hide, and knew that the result of the race had not been altogether to his liking.

'Fancy!' he grumbled. 'Old Sal! Losing to that'n! Oughn't to have run her legs off! Bah! She must 'a been a bit off colour. Why the 'ell didn't old Jim tell me? Old Sal! Ugh!'

Suddenly he raised his voice to a yell that made the hair stand upright on my head.

'Eh! You! Come out on it! D' ye hear? Come on out!'

Brad put a restraining hand on my arm, and I heard the sound of cracking thorns farther down the hedge. I then realized that Hawky's command was not addressed to us but to some-one who was not so fortunate in their choice of ditch-hides.

After this *contretemps* Hawky came by again still mumbling. 'Old Sal! The bitch her!' and took up his position by the open stile to watch the next race.

There were the same preliminaries; the same yelping whippets. Now two almost identical dogs were in the hands of the handlers, two well-balanced animals that watched with lewd eyes every movement of the man with the struggling rabbit as he moved away from the rest of the crowd. He stood upright for a moment, faced the group of people and raised the rabbit above his head triumphantly, and the eager dogs strained at the imprisoning hands and cried in a high-pitched voice, keen to kill.

The spotter bent to the ground and threw the rabbit forward, and, as it rolled over and over with the impetus of the throw, the man lifted his arms as a signal to the starter, and the dogs sped away from the handlers.

But the rabbit crouched low to the ground and would not run farther. So great was its terror that, when the spotter lifted it again and cast it forward, it rolled again and lay half dead, with closed eyes.

As the dogs drew near to the gesticulating man, he placed the toe of his heavy boot under the frightened body and lifted it in the air, and before it reached the ground the whippets were upon it, worrying savagely at the creature.

In a moment it was all over. The spotter raised both arms to signify to the judges and the betting men that there had been no race, and some of the spectators yelled to him over the field angrily, blaming him for the poorness of the sport.

I grimaced to Brad, and he signalled to me to withdraw from the ditch.

When we were safely on the other side of the hedge he spoke to me in a low voice.

'I don't like that!' he said. I felt sick. We had taken plenty of rabbits from time to time, but never in such a way. As we passed the stile where old Hawky stood on guard he looked suspiciously at us.

'What do you want?' he queried gruffly, but we did not answer until we were well out of harm's way, then Brad threw some muck-clods at him, deliberately, in a cold fury. Hawky shook his fist at us.

'You young devils!' he shouted. But Brad said nothing, and I joined him in the muck throwing.

On our way home we washed our hands at the sheep-wash, where the water was stale and scummy, until they were clean again.

The spotter was not a young man then, but he made old bones, living to be well over eighty years.

The little wizened man who helped with the rabbits saw his last race that day. He died one night soon afterwards in a thick wood with a look of inquiry on his face.

There was a shot in the darkness and Trister—leaning over his snares—rolled gently on the soft leaf mould and gazed, surprised, through the tree tops at a single star.

It was all very accidental, but very final.

All this took place in those spacious days of the seventh Edward, before the world had found its freedom.

Old Corduroy Pants was not aware of its absence, neither was Hawky, nor any of the Saturday afternoon group of whippet racers. Yet they fought for this ephemera when a poster pointed a finger at them and blowzy young wenches stuck wyandotte feathers in their coarse coats.

Long Jem, the silent shepherd, went in search of this new thing. The master's son, straight from one of the universities, had talked to Jem in the meadows of an August evening.

In those same meadows under a light sprinkling of snow the young man, gay in his new uniform, had spoken to Jem again and, in anger, had torn the wyandotte feather from the shepherd's lapel.

'Don't stand for this, Jem,' he had said, fierce eyes shining from an indignant face, but the shepherd was not indignant.

'Some gel gave it to me,' he explained. 'It's a nice feather.'

But he went with the rest. And he found this new freedom too, somewhere in a mud heap between two lines of trenches in Flanders.

The master's son came to tell Widow Wesson how her only son died.

'He was a fine soldier and a brave man,' he said as he sat in her neat kitchen, leaning forward in the hard chair, trying to make her understand.

'Wh-eer is he now?' asked the old woman, a petulant whine in her voice. 'Wh-eer is he now? Is he still soldiering?'

The young man tried again.

'He was a brave man,' he repeated, reluctant to break the awful news. 'It was this way. Our attack was beaten off and we suffered casualties. Wesson tried to bring back to our lines his wounded friend. Do you understand?' the lad pleaded.

The old lady peered at him vacantly.

'He wor a good boy,' she murmured. 'When's he coming back? It's hard on a woman on her own.'

'Mrs Wesson, you must be brave. He will not come back again.' The plunge was taken. 'He lost his life trying to save his friend.'

'Is he been shot?'

'Yes. Oh, I'm so sorry for you.'

'They bloody Germans,' the old woman said without heat.

She crouched over the fire of red gleed and looked into its depths. A few tears trickled into the cracks and crevices of her lined face.

'It's a long while since he went,' she said, a sob in her voice. 'He used to gi' me ten bob a week for his keep. I'll miss that now. Aw, dear!'

The village folk said that he was the best sheep man in the district; that he'd be hard to replace.

But Jem went humbly to heaven, or thereabouts, and the world was ten shillings the poorer.

H

A FAMILY of Irish tinkers came to camp on the common for a few days, pitching their sacking tents near to the low thorn copse in which old Goldie Taylor had his home.

They were an unhappy lot, resentful of the world and distrustful, yet there was something ineffably sad in their manner, in their intense longing for their native land and the memories that they carried.

In the evenings I sat with them by their stick fire, listening to their tales, for they were great talkers once their tongues had been loosened. And incredibly adept spinners, too, of the fine webs of which folk-tales are made.

I became aware of another world of existence outside the mundane world of human experience.

'There's whispy folk in the bogs below the hills. Little cratures that rise like a puff of stame. And they holler when you pass 'em by.'

'What sort of a noise do they make?' I asked with deep interest.

'Oh, begor! A kind of a noise . . . like . . . Aw! There's no telling! Sometimes it's one kind, sometimes another. It's all according.' The tale-teller paused.

'You'd not be disbelieving me, would you now?'

I remonstrated. 'Of course not! As if I would!'

The tinker was satisfied.

'Would they be called "will-o'-the-wisps"?' I asked. Somewhere I had heard of such things.

'Will-o'-the-whisps is ut!' the little man ejaculated. 'Ah yes! Perhaps it's the willy-whisps. I dunno! I tell you what I've seen and heard, that's all.'

He leaned forward confidingly and jerked a thumb in the direction of Goldie's shack.

'Who's the old fellow?' he asked in a low voice.

I explained that his name was Goldie Taylor; that he had lived in the shack for several years; so long in fact that he had become accepted as a regular member of the village community, although not permitted to participate in the social life thereof, for Goldie was hardly the type for any society but his own, and, truth to tell, he preferred things that way.

Like the tinker, he too had been a wanderer until, against much local opposition, he settled in the clearing in the thorn spinney. As time went on he added to the previous hutment, haphazardly yet not without some sort of plan, until there now existed a fairly comfortable dwelling-place which compared very favourably with many of the labourers' cottages down in the village.

Goldie had acquired a tin of green paint (even Peabody had been unable to prove that the old man had come by it other than honestly) and with this he had made a fair job of outside decoration.

All in all it was not a bad place.

Many attempts had been made in the past to dislodge the old man, but he stood firmly to his home and defied them.

'You shift me from here', he said, 'and you'll have to house me somewhere else. I'll go union, then the rates'll ha' to keep me!'

'But', authority protested, 'the sanitary arrangements are primitive. Positively primitive!'

'Look to our village!' retorted Goldie. 'They're no better there!' And he was right.

'You'll have to go,' they warned him and, having done their duty by the warning, left him in peace.

He picked up a living as best he could; by odd jobs around the farms, or by a bit of droving from farm to market town, trudging gently behind a herd of beasts, with all the time in the world for the journey, completely oblivious to the commotion at his rear caused by the impatient new-fangled automobiles.

Often at the road turnings there would be a little disorderliness when one half of the herd decided to go one way and the rest the other, but then Goldie would spring into action, yelling wildly and spanking at their backs with his long blackthorn wand until he had gathered them together again into a single group, and the slow journey would be continued.

The Irish tinker listened intently as I told him of Goldie, and when I had finished thrust his head towards me and said, almost in a whisper:

'Would he be having any lovo, boy? Any money, you understand?'

I drew back in alarm, for there was a bright look in the eyes of the man which startled me, a hardness which I had seen in the eyes of the weasel when it marks its game.

'You let be!' I cried angrily. 'You let be! He's all right!'

He'll not hurt you! He's got nothing! How can he have?
How can he have money? He's poor. He is, I tell you! That's
a dreadful thing you're thinking!'

I rose indignantly to my feet, but the man placed a restraining hand on my arm and pressed me to the ground again, and
as I looked at him now, in a little fear, I saw that the hard light
had gone from his eyes and laughter sat there instead.

'Whist now, man! Take it aisy! What's the cause of your
pothering? I'm not after the ould man's gould! There's plenty
where I come from, begor!'

I looked at him suspiciously.

'Then why are you tinkering for a meal? Why didn't you
stay with the gold?'

'But you see . . .' he replied. 'It ain't that aisy!' He drew
close to me and spoke confidentially.

'Listen, will you? Imagine a path that winds and winds
up'ards from the foot of the hills, upwards through the bottom
spinney until it is lost in the hillside and only a dog track is left
and that hard to see, begor! Somewhere up there, near to
where the water comes tumbling down the slope, the little folk
play at night. Ye'll not be believing me, boy, but by God it's
true! Somewhere there, behind a big stane, if you could only
find it, there's a big crock of gould, so much you've never seen
the like. Begor, boy! It only wants finding, and only the little
people look after it. And they're naught to be scared of.'

'Why hasn't it been found?' I asked. 'Why don't they dig
for it? If you know the spot, surely it's easily found? Has
anyone been to the waterfall?'

'Aye, boy! Plenty of folk have gone, but somehow they all
lose the way of it. It's the little folk, I'm thinking! They
bedevil ye and make you dream. I've not been to the hills
where the crock is hidden, but I'll be finding it one day—and
to hell with the little people!'

As he rambled on I became tired of the whole story of fairies and folk, and soon I left the tents and went to the four-acre. But I was uneasy.

I had not liked the little Irishman's attitude at all, neither had I liked the greedy look in his eyes when he had spoken of Goldie.

I did not believe for one moment that the old man had any hidden hoard, for he was too shiftless to earn more than he required for his immediate needs, and yet if the tinker had reason to think otherwise I feared that he would attempt to rob Goldie notwithstanding. Goldie would never tolerate the indignity of this and, all in all, I could see the spilling of a drop or two of blood. As long as it was the tinker's gore I did not mind, but I was afraid that the old man might come off worst, and this worried me not a little, for I liked Goldie, cantankerous old devil though he was.

'Did you know that there's a lot of gold in Ireland?' I asked Brad later in the day.

'There's a lot in England too if you can get hold of it!' he retorted. 'Who's been talking to you?'

I told him the tinker's tale and he was scornful.

'Little folk! Little folk guarding the gold! What rot! We've gold in England too, I tell you, and it ain't guarded by little folk. It's guarded by big 'uns, in uniform. And they're not much like fairies either. More like old Peabody. What a lot of nonsense! Why do you listen to these poshrats! They're all daft!'

I told him of the tinker's questions regarding Goldie's supposed wealth, and he became serious.

'That scum means business, you know. He wouldn't ask things like that unless he meant to have a go. I don't like it.'

For a long time he sat in silence, lost in thought. I could tell that the information I had conveyed had made a deep impression on him, for he too was fond of old Goldie, despite the fact that they had often quarrelled about the ownership of a snared rabbit which one or the other had claimed as his.

The old man had been useful to us in the winter months too, after Michaelmas when the birds were fair game. He told us of the movements of linnet flocks, of goldfinches on the thistle heads, and greenies on the stubble.

'Bring your twigs, boyo! There's a fine bullfinch in the sloe bushes.'

I think he took a delight in watching us at bird-taking, for, when he saw the finches on the lime, he would rub his hands together and chortle and hurry forward to stroke the little captives, chucking them under their chin feathers and clucking like a hen with chicks.

'Tuck, tuck! Cluck, cluck! There's a grand little fellow! There's grand little things for you!'

When Brad asked him to accept a lovely poldfinch cock, and offered to make him a wicker cage for it, old Goldie hesitated and looked long at the beautiful bird before shaking his head.

'No!' he said ruefully. 'No! I'd ha' to let him go within a week. You can't keep a lovely thing caged, boyo! It only becomes ordinary if you do. Birds and women; it's all the same.' And, as though not to offend by his refusal, he said: 'I like to see 'em, you know. I like to see you catch 'em. That's clever, that is; real clever. But I'd not like to keep him. God, boyo!' He turned to me. 'I had a week in the "big house" once. Aw! No matter what for! I saw the sky through a little window in the wall. Gor! I never thought it could be so far away. A week, boyo! You try to imagine it!' He pointed an accusing finger at me. 'You! Out of the meadows for a week, and the sky a little hole in the wall!' He shook his head sorrowfully.

'You keep the bird, boyo! It's a good bird.'

We, in our turn, used to keep Goldie informed when we found new burrows in the ditchside banks where the rabbits had become established and where snares were of little use. Then the old man would come along with his pink-eyed ferret and half a dozen purse-nets, and in a short time there would be no rabbits left in the holes.

Sometimes he would call at the tent on his way back to the shack and leave a coney there, but that did not happen often, for he had a ready market in the village for all that he could catch.

Brad rose abruptly.

'Come on!' he commanded.

'To Goldie?' I inquired.

He nodded. 'I'm not happy about that tinker. He's a bad lot! We'll tell Goldie all about it. Better that he should know just in case the Irishman tries anything on tonight.'

And so we went, not over the common where the tinker's tents were pitched, but on the low road, along the old mere, the rutty cart-track that passed close by the end of the black-thorn scrub.

We shouted to the old man as we approached the copse, and he told us to go to hell.

'It's me, Goldie,' yelled Brad. 'I'm coming through,' and we pushed our way between the thorny wands of sloe, along a narrow track which led to the clearing.

There were twenty yards or so of open ground in the middle of the spinney, and on this space of green turf stood Goldie's habitation.

As we emerged from the bushes the old man came from the crude house, and there was grim menace in his approach which disappeared as soon as he recognized us.

'Why, boyo! What are you doing here? I've got nowt, you know. No use you coming to me for owt!' This we knew to be a defensive measure.

'It's all right,' answered Brad. 'We haven't come for anything. Let's go inside or somewhere. We've got something to tell you.'

'Wait a minute!' replied Goldie. 'I ain't much for conies now, you know. Bit late in the season. Does in kindle and bucks skinny!'

'It's not that,' said Brad. He turned to me.

'You tell him, boyo!'

We were approaching the hut now and Goldie beckoned us to a seat on the ground, but out of the corner of my eye I detected a movement within the shack, a surreptitious withdrawing of a head from one of the windows, and at this I stood up again and looked hard at Goldie.

'There's someone in the shack!' I accused. 'Who is it?'

He shrugged his shoulders but did not reply to my question.

'Who is it?' I demanded again. 'I'm not staying. Come on, Brad! I don't like this. There's someone there.'

'Wait now, boyo!' soothed Goldie. 'Wait now. What's the matter with you? It's nothing to hurt!'

But I was not satisfied, and began to regret that we had interfered in the old man's affairs. There was something not quite straightforward about the whole business; and now the lurking shadow behind the curtain of the window.

I backed away towards the narrow track through the blackthorn scrub, and Brad—puzzled now—came towards me.

As we went slowly away from the hut, watchful, alert, I kept a suspicious eye on the old man, for I had come to mistrust him almost as much as I had earlier mistrusted the Irish tinker, but he suddenly laughed loudly and beckoned to the hut.

'Come on out, you!' he called. 'Come on, I say! Come here.'

He turned to me and grinned.

'You silly 'ellion!' he swore. 'It's only my mate!'

From the doorway came a tall stooping figure, a giant of a man who dwarfed Goldie.

'Good laws!' ejaculated Brad.

'Big Tom!' I yelled in surprise. 'Big Tom! Where have you come from?'

'He's my mate!' said Goldie. 'We'm teamed up. He'd nowhere to go so he's coming wi' me. We'll make a do of it! Don't take no notice of him. He's a bit flummoxed yet!'

Thus it was that the ill-assorted couple had come together— the garrulous Goldie and the truculent giant.

In the little while that we were with them it was obvious that the little man was the master. Tom looked to his wants as he had attended to those of his mad mother, fetching and carrying, anticipating Goldie's wishes like a big obedient dog.

'Come and sit down, Tammy!' invited Goldie, and the big man squatted by his side. We spoke of his mother and how she had passed away, and Tom looked sullenly at the ground without speaking.

'Where have you been all the time?' I asked. 'Why did you leave the village?'

'He'm been mixed up wi' a bunch of didikois!' old Goldie explained. 'A poor lot. It's no life for a lad like him! He's bin use to better things so he came to me.'

Big Tom nodded mechanically without raising his head and Brad grinned at Goldie's naïveté.

'What a pair!' he murmured, loud enough for Goldie to hear. 'What a pair!'

The old man glared at my brother.

'We'm all right,' he said slowly. 'Me and mi' mate. We'm all right!' and suddenly he placed a skinny hand on the big man's arm as though reassuring him, and Tom lowered his head still farther until it almost slumped on his chest.

From that moment an incredible friendship was sealed which lasted till the end of their lives; where there was Goldie, there would be Big Tom, his silent, sullen guard.

They worked in the fields together, the giant doing his share and the greater part of Goldie's too. They drove cattle from the market, travelling side by side along the country lanes, the little man—more nimble than his companion despite the difference in their ages—running on ahead to check the cattle at the side turnings.

When Goldie infrequently stayed to drink at the market town pubs Tom would stay too, sitting on the cobbled pavement, his back propped against the wall, waiting for his mate. And when Goldie came, a little unsteadily, from the hostelry, Tom would take him gently by the arm and lead him home.

'I'll not do it again, Tammy,' the old man would say. 'It's a bad thing to do.' But neither by word nor look would Tom reproach him. He accepted things as they were, without question.

'Ye'll go wi' me if they folk turn us out, Tammy?' old Goldie asked anxiously, after the authorities had reissued their threat.

'We'll get a van, Tammy. You'll go wi' me, eh?'

'I'll go!' answered Big Tom, slowly nodding his head.

'It'll be rough, Tammy. Terrible rough, 'specially in the bad times. And you a house-wallah too. But you'd go wi' me, Tammy?'

'I'd go!' came the slow reply. 'I'd go wi' you.'

But the need did not arise. They were left in peace.

'Goldie,' I said, after we had settled on the greensward. 'Goldie! I've something to tell you.'

The old man turned his head sharply, like an inquisitive bird, and his eyes shone as I related my suspicions of the tinker.

'He's after your gold,' I said, and Goldie laughed loudly.

'I wish him luck,' he said joyously. 'You think he'll come tonight?'

I replied that I had no reason to think that the danger was so near.

'But watch out!' I warned. 'I'm sure he means business.'

'He'll come tonight if he comes at all,' mused Goldie. 'He's moving off tomorrow. Oh, I know! The flattie'—thus did he slander Peabody—'has given him tonight, then he's got to clear off. I know! And he's after mi' ha'pence, eh? The dirty hindity!'

He turned to us.

'You go now. Don't come back again this side of the morning! I'll set a snare for that Irish mush that'll larn him summat for a while. Go now!'

We turned from the two men and went back through the scrub.

'I'd not like to be the tinker,' chuckled Brad. 'Goldie'll lay something for him if I can judge, and it'll be hot!'

We talked of these possibilities as we walked towards my tent and of the strange and sudden friendship of the two strange men, but could not have guessed of the dreadful things which were to happen that night in Goldie's blackthorn spinney.

When we had gone Goldie called Big Tom to him and explained his plans. They drove willow pegs—thick as a man's wrist—into the ground at regular intervals until there were four rows of short posts stretching along the open length of ground that divided the thorn scrub from the hutments, the first of these rows being about ten yards from the scrub edge.

From an inner room Big Tom brought two rolls of wire, one of which was thin and whippy, strong enough to hold an ox; the other barbed with ferocious spikes.

The thin trip-wire was run in a line straight across the clearing, about five inches from the ground, securely attached to the first row of willow pegs. Another strand was affixed to the second row of willows, two feet to the rear of the first row and a few inches higher. Farther back still Goldie ran two more lines, of barbed wire, both some fifteen inches high and about three feet apart. These two rows were connected up by a series of criss-cross patterns of barbed wire until the affair looked like a weird kind of trampoline.

It was almost dark before the men had finished their task. Many times Goldie tested the strength of the wires and the exact height of the first trip-wire before he expressed his satisfaction.

He walked to the gap in the blackthorn which led to the clearing and peered from there to his hut.

'Yes!' he said at last. 'Yes! He'll come through there. He'll run across the open ground to the shelter of the huts, and then the wire'll have him.'

He again explained the plan to Tom, who had helped to erect the snare without really knowing its purpose, and at last the big man nodded his head to indicate that he understood.

'Cut a couple of sloe wands!' commanded Goldie. 'Thick 'uns. About four foot long! We'll gi' him gold, the Irish hindity!'

After this careful preparation there was nothing to do but wait, and this they did in silence.

They sat in the darkness, for Goldie possessed no means of illumination, and the older man dozed on his rough bed from time to time. But not Big Tom. He sat awkwardly on a bundle of sacking in a corner of the room, relaxed as a resting dog, yet alert, listening.

An owl called from the scrawny elm and another answered, and their cries came eerily through the night, out of place in the quietness of the common, but Tom did not move.

A mouse screamed in a corner of the room, and a hurried

scuffle took place in among a pile of paper and rubbish there
as one urgent little male chased his mate in the darkness, but
it was as nothing to Tom. His ears were strained for sounds
farther away.

A whimper of noise came from the tents on the common,
the thin, muffled cry of a waking infant, protesting at being
disturbed, but it soon ended in a slobbering gurgle as the tired
child was put to the soothe of a feeding breast.

Tom put out a hand and placed it on Goldie's arm.

'What's up?' inquired the old man, somewhat dreamily.
He put his head in his hands for a moment then, recovered
from his nap, asked:

'Is he away yet? Where is he?'

'Just left the tents,' said Tom softly. 'Heard a nipper
squeak. Listen!'

Goldie walked quietly to the open doorway and waited,
stick in hand.

THE LITTLE Irishman swore when the child cried in the night,
and thrust an elbow into the ribs of the woman at his side.

'Keep it quiet, will you now?' he snarled.

'Ye'll be taking your knife?' she inquired in a whisper.

'Whist, woman! No!' he replied impatiently. 'I'll not be

seeking trouble. He's only a little ould man! I'll take mi'
stick! If he's noisy I'll tap him behind the earhole. There'll be
no chinger. I'll put him to slape for a bit!'

'You'll find your way?' she asked.

'Sure enough! I'll find it!' he answered. 'I'll go round the
spinney by the ould mucky road. There's a gap in the bushes
there. Oh, begor! I've had a look round!'

He turned when he reached the tent opening.

'Keep the chavies quiet over there!' he commanded,
indicating the occupants of the other tents, and she grunted
assent.

It was a soft dark night; a velvet night, with so little light
that the tips of the trees were hardly discernible against the
background of sky, but the little tinker moved adroitly along
the common, almost sensing the obstacles in his way and
avoiding them.

Again the owl called from the elm, a long-drawn-out note,
and again her mate answered, but with a sharper accent.

'Quick-ick-ick-ick,' and she flew on soft wings to him,
passing close enough to the skulking tinker to make him swear
as the ghostly wings went by.

He froze into immobility and the hair lifted on his neck
when a late-mating vixen howled in the darkness, and
cursed under his breath when he realized the cause of the
horrible din.

'God ha' mercy!' he blasphemed. 'There's weirdies about
tonight. It's a hormy night!'

Carefully he picked his way along the mere road, feeling
each step with his foot lest he should slip and turn an ankle,
until at last he came to the gap in the bushes which led to
Goldie's shack.

Stealthily he pushed through the thorns, treading with great
caution, for he knew that the crack of a rotted twig could give

him away, and soon he had reached the end of the sloe pathway; before him lay the few yards of ground which separated him from Goldie's shack.

The tinker crouched low and looked upwards to the sky, and there, faintly silhouetted against the blackness, he saw the dark outline of the hutments, and mentally marked the position.

He rested for a moment before gathering himself for the sprint across the clearing.

The blood flew to his head as he began his run for, even in such darkness, he felt naked away from the shelter of the thorn bushes and was anxious to be away from the open spaces.

On the soft turf he sped on tiptoe, noiseless as a cat. Less than a dozen paces and he tripped over something on the ground. As he lunged forward his rear foot to help recover his balance, that too caught the second of the tripping wires, and the tinker put out a hand to save himself.

But there was no avoiding the snare. His hand closed on the higher strands of barbed wire and a gash of skin was torn from them. His face was ripped open in a long weal, and as he struggled to free himself his clothes became hopelessly entangled on the mattress of vicious spikes.

'God!' he prayed, feeling the blood course down his cheek. He lifted his head from the wire and tried to find the ground with his feet so that he could stand upright again and disentangle himself from the holding barbs, but the cunning trap soon had him down again, and he lay exhausted, sprawled like a spatchcocked fowl.

Two dark figures loomed up from the gloom, two grim figures that bore down upon him from the direction of the huts.

The tinker did not speak: he knew the game was up.

Goldie thrashed at him with his long blackthorn stick as he lay helpless on the wire, and Big Tom looked on silently.

Time and time again the little man flogged at the prisoner until at long last his arm grew tired and he could strike no more.

'Take him off!' Goldie said to the impassive Tom, who unceremoniously plucked the half-fainting tinker from the wire.

'Bring him along!' commanded the old man. 'We'd better take him home!'

The giant lifted the tinker in his arms as though he were a child and followed Goldie through the blackthorn bushes. All the way along the rutted road the limp figure in Tom's arms groaned, and the big man shook him gently.

Over the common they went, upwards to the tents, and as they approached the infant whimpered again, and the woman called in alarm.

'Hey, there! Who's there? Who are you now?'

Goldie motioned to Tom and the man threw his burden on to the squat sacking tent, which collapsed under the weight of the inert tinker.

The infant cried again and the woman screamed, but her cries were muffled under the fallen sacking.

Other voices were raised from the rest of the tents, and soon there was pandemonium on the common.

'Mi' man!' came a stifled voice from out of the mix-up. 'Mi' man! What ev they done at him now?'

Goldie and Big Tom walked slowly back to their home, satisfied with the night's work.

The next morning, when Brad and I called on the little man, there was little evidence of the events of the previous night. We noticed that the tinkers' tents had gone from the common, and my brother looked at me significantly.

'Goldie said that Peabody was having them moved off today, you know,' I reminded him.

I

When we arrived at the clearing Big Tom was struggling with the last willow post which still remained in the ground.

Near to the huts were two neatly coiled rolls of wire and the rest of the posts, all carefully laid out, awaiting storage.

'Hallo!' greeted Brad. 'What's up?'

'Up?' repeated Goldie. 'What do you mean?'

'You know well enough what I mean!' said my brother. 'What's all this paraphernalia? Have you started to keep sheep or something?' He was purposely prevaricating.

'We keep nowt here!' retorted Goldie. 'Leastways not if we can get rid of it.'

I could stand this by-play no longer.

'Did the Irishman come last night, Goldie? Did he come for your gold?' I asked anxiously.

The old man looked at me and smiled. Softly he said:

'We had visitors last night, boyo! We gave 'em a bit of a reception. We'm just clearing up now.'

He looked over to the common, the empty common, where a thin wisp of smoke wound idly upwards from the dying embers of the tinker's fire.

And he spat.

A CROCK of gold indeed! Who would search for a crock of gold? There was gold in plenty in the crook of the brook where the kingcups grew. Aye! and all polished too, not the dingy buried stuff with the muck of a lifetime on it, but all newly minted and handsome.

With each guinea-petal a gem-beetle could be bought and kept for a moment or two, and as the jewel flew away so could the gilt be thrown after it, prodigally, for there was much more.

On the bankside of the silver stream lay a carpet of gold that money could not buy, all the wealth of the world's treasury in

the patch of celandine which gleamed in the slanting sunlight;
and that didn't want digging for; all one had to do was to
stretch out in a summer sleep on the soft cool grass, and wait
for the flowers to wake.

There were riches in plenty here, and jewels passed from
bloom to bloom in the sun.

I had no use for a crock of gold, nor for the tinker who told
such tales. My world was mine, and all things were free, and
gold was made but to dust my dingy shoes or to paint my
naked feet with buttercup pollen when I went over the wet
grass in the morning on my way to the cattle-drink where I
washed. Such lordliness is possible to youth.

I saw less of Brad than usual on these lazy days of the year.
Sometimes he came to the tent in the early evening, but often
he left before the blackbirds began to fidget and I, almost
drugged to incomprehension by the wonder of the season, let
him go without question. His going was no more than the
flight of a bee; there were so many more in the clover-heads,
why should I miss one?

There was little school for me, for now I was beyond the
age when truancy mattered very much to the authorities.
Instead I idled the days away by the waterside, picking the
flowers to pieces, chewing the young sour-grass leaves and
tormenting the birds with imitation.

Few people came to the brook meadows and, because of
that, I was never lonely, for it is noisy folk that empty the fields
and the hedgerows; that quieten the birds at their song and
cause the dancing weasel to hide in the brickbats by the side of
the little cattle bridge.

There is nothing in the world when there are only people.
It becomes a lonesome place, all phantoms and dull talking,
and neither mating music nor quiet sub-song. There is no
voice like the fluting blackbird when he sings to his mate

through the orchestra of bee-song and sedge-whisper; no voice like the ring-dove, full cropped with the farmer's grain, crooning contentedly in the swelling elm.

The narrow-boats went their slow way along the canal, quietly for the most part, except when the old mare forgot her job and allowed the towrope to slacken. Then a rasping voice would ring out from the boat, a snarl of command to the urchin in charge of the dozy animal, and he in turn would yell a piercing 'Gee-e-e-e. You!' to the mare.

But the noise all came from the deep-cut banks near to the tunnel entrance and was muffled to us on the brook-side and not sharp enough to cause alarm, but only to halt the birds at their song momentarily.

I heard the harsh squawk of a frightened bird and went downstream to a clump of scrawny hawthorn bushes from which direction the sound came. As I approached the noise became almost continuous, and I heard a man swear.

'What's the matter?' I inquired, seeing a figure behind the bush. I recognized him immediately, for he was a familiar figure in the fields, a young man of little intelligence who worked a little but wandered more; an unstable character, harmless but pretty well useless. But who was I to judge?

In his left hand he held a young jackdaw, a flabby pin-feathered creature that had been from the nest but a few days. With thumb and forefinger the youth held open the bird's bill, forcing its mouth wide and endeavouring, with the same thumb and finger, to obtain a hold on the bird's pointed tongue.

In the other hand he held a silver sixpence, sharpened on one side to form a cutting edge, and with this weapon was trying to slit the tongue of his prisoner.

For a moment or so I watched him saw away at the quivering member, then gently took the bird from him.

'Let me have it!' he protested. 'You let me have it, boyo!

I'll mek it talk! It'll talk when I've split his tongue, you see! Let me have my bird, boyo!'

I shook my head reprovingly.

'Don't slit his tongue,' I said slowly. One had to be precise with Leffer or he would not understand.

'Don't slit his tongue. It'll make him dumb. Dumb, see? It can't talk if you cut his chops!'

He looked at me in amazement. 'You! You don't know nowt!' he accused. 'It's got to ha' its tongue cut to mek it talk. You don't know nowt! Gimme my bird!'

I held the daw out of reach of his grasping hand, and when he rose, pink of face and furious, to take the bird from me I threw it in the air and, clumsily, it flew squawking over the meadows to the spinney on the hill.

Leffer knocked me down for my interference and made my nose bleed, and I wondered if it was all worth while—the lunatic lad and the gross daw squab, neither of which would be of much use in the world.

I helped Leffer to gather a few flowers—clovers and lambs'-toes—with which he made a ring-posy, and soon the incident of the bird was forgotten.

He was so engrossed in his work when I left that he did not notice my going.

Leffer came to the brook only infrequently; he preferred the canal banks where the kecks grew, the umbels of which he could use for the framework of his posies.

At odd intervals too the moucher came to gather watercress, but he was a silent man and made little difference to the countryside beyond muddying the clear stream for a while as he walked awkwardly in the mud to pick the fresh heads of the plant.

Little Crooked Willie, the cripple, came to the rickety fence which divided the brook meadow from the footpath field, but he could only stand and stare up the length of the stream, for the fence was a barrier which he could not climb, yet which Brad and I could vault with ease. Crooked Willie had often watched us do this, and each time I almost felt the envy in his look.

Only few of us went to the little brook, and perhaps we were all as crooked as Willie in one way or another. I felt that the others were interlopers there and greatly resented their presence on what I considered my preserves.

The days were so long that from three o'clock dawn to eleven o'clock dark seemed an age, and yet night came too soon and the waste of sleep was begrudged.

For hours on end I lay with the sun on my back, head cupped in hands, watching a hillock of ants repairing their home after it had been partially destroyed by a lumbering cow. All seemed disorder at first, and yet each oval egg, each larval shape, was gathered up and taken into the brown crumbs of earth, below the crushed leaves of the lemon hawkweed, out of sight of the prying eyes of the laughing yaffle.

All through the long sunny morrow I lazed again, watching the red-backed bees taking the honeydew from the white clovers, unwinding their hair-spring tongues to search for the sweetness that lay in the heart of each floret; counting the times they came until the sun took a hold of me and the scents stole my senses. Then I slept fitfully in the music of the interminable insects, waking to find the bees still at work, many now, with little bags of yellow pollen on their legs, bags of gold that had come to me with no asking.

A grass-snake sometimes kept me not too close company, writhing through the short grass to the hummock at the top of the bank; there to lie in the warmth of the sunshine, coiled on a platter of dried, chaffy cow-dung. And neither he nor the playing weasel took notice of me, for I had become part of the landscape, a rag cast carelessly on the grass. But the wood-pigeon knew better. He swerved abruptly away from the spot where I lay; and the old crow—alive to such a warn-ing—croaked hoarsely to his mate nesting in the high elm tree.

On these days I drank at the brook and ate when day was done, for in the long hours there was no time for food, so much life could be missed by interruption.

'Where've you been?' Brad asked when I arrived at the tent to find him already there.

'To the brooklet,' I replied. 'To the shallows where the blackbirds bathe.'

'What! All day? What did you see?'

'Er . . . Some bees. . . .' I hesitated, realizing that my answer must seem inadequate to him.

'Bees!' exploded Brad.

'On some clover,' I added, beginning to feel uncomfortable.

'All day watching bees!' replied my brother in heavy reproof. 'All day, and bumble-bees of all things. And that's all you've seen? No rabbits or anything? Aw dear! The sun's no good to you.' He looked at me closely. 'You ain't bad, are you?'

I could not try to explain now. I knew that he was too sane to understand, and I felt a little out of my depth.

For a long time he sat with me in the four-acre, and we soon talked of other things; of the nests and the loveliness of eggs.

'The dunnock's the best!' affirmed Brad. 'Blue as the sky.'

I looked at him in surprise, for it was unlike him to be over-generous in his praise of anything; but I agreed.

We spoke of bird flight and the wonder of song as the thrush sang from the haw bush above, and then, as was usual, we sat quite quietly, listening to all the sounds of the evening again;

and we found the world a good place; the world of the
meadows, anyway.

The creaky gate of Wranglands broke across birdsong and
lamb-call, waking me from my daydream, and I rose and went
over to the fire to put the billy on the freshly lit sticks.

'I'm hungry!' I declared. 'You'll stay and have a taste of
food of course?' But, to my surprise, Brad refused.

'No, thanks!' he said. 'I've got to be off now.' He looked a
trifle embarrassed.

'But', I protested, 'it's early yet! Where've you got to go?
I say, what's up? It's early yet, you know.'

But what I said made no difference.

'I've got to go,' was all that he would say. 'I'll come round
tomorrow,' and with that he went, leaving me very puzzled.

Soon the footsteps of the young couples crunched on the
black ash path that led to the low bridge, and subdued giggles
woke up the little owls, and they called to each other over the
meadows, quietly, in mockery. And when darkness fell on the
fields I went to my bed, satisfied with the day.

The next day there were cold rook-pies to be delivered to
the young town people who had built a fine white house on the
hillside overlooking the wide valley. Being so young and
immature in country ways they were determined to experience
all the strange foods that they had been told existed in the
country, both good and bad; and they must have been strong
in digestion to have absorbed some of the rubbish that the
villagers fed to them (at a price of course) before they came to
the delicacies which my mother provided. After becoming
acquainted with her viands and her cooking, they trusted no
other.

Brad brought the order to me soon after daybreak.

'There's squab-pie for the Costellos,' he said. 'You're to
take it.'

I looked at him inquiringly.

'I'm to town wi' the milk float,' he explained. 'Smithers has offered me the job. There's extra money in it, you know.'

Brad was fast becoming a young man, a workman in fact, knowing his own worth to his casual employers who were very aware of his usefulness.

He went from the four-acre, whistling shrilly in the clear morning air as he walked springily over the meadows towards Smithers' farm. I collected the pies from home and was given certain instructions.

'Tell the young lady to warm them through. Only to warm them for a while, you understand? They have already been cooked. Tell her to put a half onion in the oven with them! That will keep the pastry from catching, and add a little flavour too. Not too hot an oven, you understand?'

I nodded and departed with the wicker basket over my arm.

'Tell her I've a few mushrooms!' she shouted after me when I was half way down the drive, and I waved my hand to indicate that I had heard.

The goods were duly delivered to the pleasant and grateful young woman, and all the instructions forgotten, but she laughed and said she thought she knew what to do.

Tentatively she offered me a copper or two for my trouble, as she had often done before, but hastily withdrew her hand and apologized kindly when she saw the flush on my face.

'You'll have a drink then, eh? Come on now! It's herb beer.'

I suppose I must have looked somewhat dubiously at her when she made the offer, but the matter was settled when she said: 'It was made by your mother, boyo!'

She was a kind soul, I suppose, but I could never get used to the quickness of her ways, her abrupt movements and mannerisms that scared birds and animals away for half a mile around. Even the staid old pony mare, grazing in the adjoining field, would snort and shy when she came to the garden to enjoy the sun. She appeared to move in jerks, not smoothly as do other things in the fields.

A ploughboy trudges slowly over the rough ground behind his team, head and shoulders bent over the stilts of his plough, a clumsy figure in the cobbled streeets, but moving with ease over the turned clods, smoothly, softly; not a movement of hand or body sudden enough to startle the dragging horses or the following rooks quarrelling in the furrows at his heels. That is as it is. The speed of the country is the speed of a grazing cow, or the pace of a flock of ewes with lambs at heel, walking over the hard metalled road from fold to feeding close. That is the pace to which impatient man must become attuned.

The lady had not yet settled to that pace.

After my errand I sauntered over the ridge of the hills, breathing the pure air of the morning and enjoying the view that the occupants of the white house had paid so much to obtain.

Like a green grass-snake, a close-growing wood climbed the near hill, reaching almost to the old cart-road which passed along the escarpment.

The valley below was laid out in a wonderful patchwork of green meadows alternating with little ten-acre fields of plough; all set square and neat as though they had been painted into the picture.

On the farther slope, across the valley, nestled a little village of grey stone, snug in the tall trees of the rambling manor house, and the spire of a church rose surprisingly between two lank lombardy poplars.

Out in the village fields, away from the compactness of the stone houses, stood little red-brick barns and farm buildings, dotting the brown and green landscape like toys from a penny bazaar.

Beyond the white house where the young couple lived, beyond a turn in the hills, there was a field of gorse which made me think of the tinker's crock of gold. Throughout the winter it flowered, miserly, but when the chiff-chaff came there was a bank full of bloom and a perfume that was heavy in the valley, as sweet and penetrating as a field of beans in summer; and now the linnets were building in the low, prickly bushes, deep beyond where the yellow flowers grew, in among the fierce thorns.

The red-throated cock bird sang in the scent of the gorse whilst his mate, uncomplaining, made her nest on this warm sunny day.

There was a break in the hill where, many years before, the local Territorial Association had had a rifle range, a deep cleft in the hillside into which men used to fire at dummy figures, in preparation for a less unreal moment.

For many years the butts had remained unused, and now all that was left was the untidy cutting in the grass bank, half full of fallen gravel and old tin cans over which nature had drawn a veil of elder and hawthorn.

Things were a little overgrown beyond the bend in the hills; the spinneys and the fields; the hedgerows and the roadside verge; but all such lushness only added to the beauty of the place.

Nettles and kecks, herriff and jack-in-the-hedge grow there as though by right, as though they had equal privilege with the Romanies who often pulled their painted bow-topped wagons on to the wide verge and turned their piebald ponies on to the grass to graze. The sprawling hills were as well known to the 'tatcho rom' as they were to the less desirable mumpers and didikois.

There was a wonderful view, let that be said—was it not for this that the Costellos had paid such a fancy price?—but I turned away.

The distance from one hilltop to the next, across the deep valley, was too far for me to contemplate; I could see too much of the world, and so I turned away from it and went downwards again to the snug meadows by the canal side.

A few sheep gazed blandly at me as I passed by, and the lead-ewe moved away towards a small hummock of manure upon which the lambs were playing. As she moved the bell at her neck jangled unmusically, but the flock took little notice of the noise. It was not night and there were no foxes to fear.

Soon time ceased to have meaning again now that I was near to the four-acre, for there is no register of hours in those particular fields except the length of one's own shadow and the hand on which it appears; or the folding of the goatsbeard and the pimpernel petals; no timepiece but the dandelion clock, one puff and all the hours of a day are gone.

All through the afternoon there had been a sleepiness in the world, and only the yellow-hammers spoke dreamily from the hedgetops. Even the brook-sparrows and willow-warblers had rested in the heat of the day.

But now, after the school hours in the village, the children's voices awakened the birds again, and soon there was plenty of sound.

Old Smithers stalked swiftly over the grass field towards his laid hayfield and yelled as he approached the gateway, and soon he was remonstrating angrily with a soldier and a scant-clad girl whom he had found lying in the long mowing grass.

'You keep out!' he warned them. 'You keep out, d'ye hear? You might do a lot of damage!'

The pair looked at the ground. Embarrassment showed on the girl's face in a suffused flush, but the soldier recovered some of his composure and apologized to the farmer.

'I'm sorry, sir. I wasn't thinking of the hay,' he said, and Smithers grudgingly accepted the excuse.

I came up to the farmer as the couple walked away.

'Rare thing!' he said, turning to me. 'Young fools! Can do no end of damage. Silly young fools!'

But as he watched them swinging over the meadows, hand in hand, there was envy in his ageing heart.

BRAD did not come to the tent in the evening. For an hour I waited by the stick fire; for longer than an hour, until the hedgehog came grunting from the hedge-stoles searching for mating worms brought up by the dew on the grass; until the huge sun had settled down behind the elm in Amberdale. Then I went to the Ramshorn gate to look for him.

There was little noise in the evening now, only the incessantly noisy blackbird, hedge-hopping; and as I leaned on the lichened rail of the gate my thoughts strayed kindly to the time when I had stood in that same place parting from Mary, and a little clutching came to my throat.

A fox went by, treading carefully on the padded mud of the

gateway, and he curled back his lip in a silent snarl when he caught my scent, but I doubt if he saw me leaning there, so quiet was I.

'There was a day . . .' I thought, and then dared think no more.

A brown owl called. 'Who-o-o-o!' But there was no answer and, silent of wing, it passed low overhead on its way to the tunnel bushes; and I dared not think of the tunnel bushes.

The lower gate opened and a youth and maid stepped out on to the black ash path. They walked forward for a little way, not together, but separated by the width of the path.

Suddenly the girl bent and plucked a daisy head which she playfully threw at the boy who, joining in the game, made an exaggerated show of dodging the pellet.

She ran nimbly over the ridge and furrow of the field and picked more flowers, and when he ran towards her she turned away and fled over the grass.

The chase did not last long, nor, I suspect, was it intended to. After a few strides the boy caught up with her and, when he would have placed a hand on her shoulder, she turned suddenly and fell into his arms, laughing and breathless, and there she remained for a while, closely held.

They walked back again to the ash path and now no inch of distance separated them. Proudly the youth went with his willing captive, his arm encircling her waist, towards the low bridge.

And suddenly, as I stood there dreaming, the incongruity of it all struck me.

The youth with the girl was my brother, Brad.